Tales of Old

Other counties in this series include:

Avon
Berkshire
Buckinghamshire
Cambridgeshire
Devon
East Anglia
Essex
Gloucestershire
Hampshire
Herefordshire
Hertfordshire
Kent
Leicestershire
Lincolnshire
Norfolk
Northamptonshire
Nottinghamshire
Oxfordshire
Shropshire
Somerset
Stratford
Suffolk
Surrey
Sussex
Warwickshire
Wiltshire
Worcestershire

Tales of Old Bedfordshire

Adrian Gray

With Illustrations by Don Osmond

COUNTRYSIDE BOOKS
NEWBURY, BERKSHIRE

First Published 1991

Reprinted 1999, 2002

COUNTRYSIDE BOOKS
3 CATHERINE ROAD
NEWBURY, BERKSHIRE

To view our complete range of books,
please visit us at
www.countrysidebooks.co.uk

ISBN 1 85306 152 2

Produced through MRM Associates Ltd., Reading
Typeset by Paragon Typesetters, Sandycroft, Chester
Printed by J. W. Arrowsmith Ltd., Bristol

For Andrew Gray, with whom I
share a Bedfordshire ancestry

Contents

BEDFORDSHIRE — The map overleaf is by John Speede, and shows the county as it was in the early seventeenth century.

BEDFORD SHIRE
AND THE SITUATION OF BEDFORD
described
with the armes of thos Honorable Fami lyes that have borne ye titles of Dukes and Earls thereof.
Ingelram Coucy Erle of Bedford
Iohn Russell Erle of Bedford
In the yere of our redemption 1399. the first of January, and 22 of King R.2. in this Countie, nere to the towne of Harwood, the Rivir Ouse suddaynly stayd her course, and divided it selfe soe, that for the space of 3. miles the wonted Chanell thereof laye drye, to the great amazement of the beholders, and eversince observed as a prodigious token or foreshewing of that great and lamentable division in the Kingdom, betwixt the families of York and Lancaster, which the next yere followed and continewed the tyme of 90. whole yeres together with bloudshend and losse.
Iodocus Hondius Caelavit
Anno Domini 1610
PART OF NORTHAMPTON SHIRE
PART OF BUCKINGHAM SHYRE
PART OF
Occidens
Oulney
Newport paganell
Hargrave
Covington
Tilbrok
Nether Dene
Shelton
Over Dene
Yelden
Swineshead
Newton
Higham Parke
Melchborne
STODDEN HUN
Ryseley
Knotting
Wimyngton
Poddington
Souldroppe
Farndysh
Sharnbrock
Thurley
Wodhill
Bletneshoe
Elmerham
Chellington
Harwood
Patenham
Carleton
Mylton
WYLLY HUND.
Bradfeld
Turvye
Ocley
Clapham
Newneton
Steventon
Brumham
Biddenham
Ouse flu.
Kempston
Astwood
Stageden
Wotton
Crawley
REDBORNSTOKE HUN.
Cranfeld
Merston
Sawford
Holcot
Myllbrok
Brokburn park
Steppingley
Wodden
Beckering park
Ashley Guise
Husbond Crawley
Segnowals
Flitwick
MANSHEAD. HUN.
Woburne
Eversholt
Woburn Abbey
Great Brikhill
Pottesgrove
Milton Brian
Tuddington
Battlesdon
Chalgrave
Hockley
Lynchlad
Egginton
Tilsworth
Leyghton
Grove
Billington
Stanbridge
Totternall
Eaton
Slapton
Edlesboro

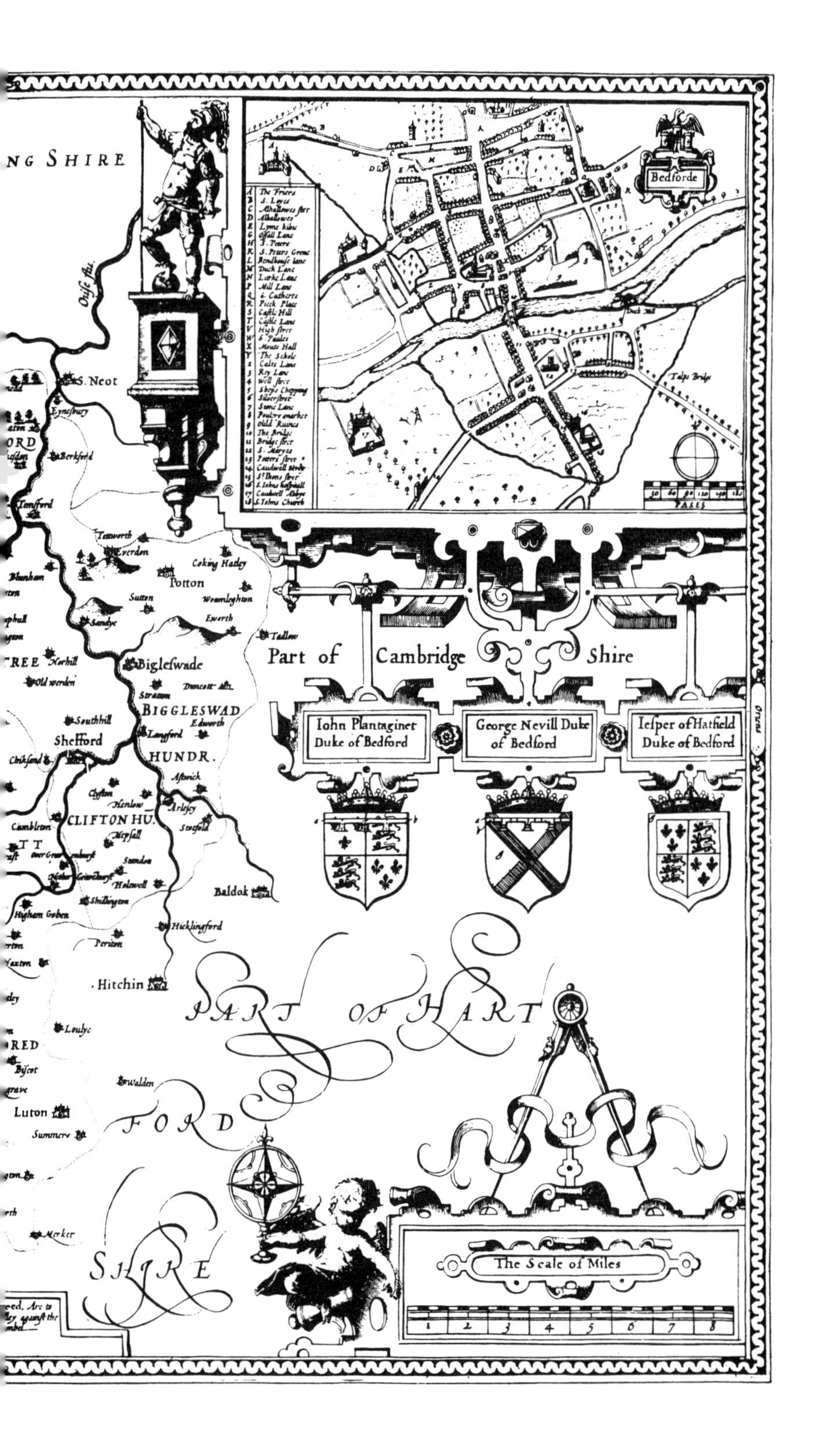
NG SHIRE
Bedforde
Part of Cambridge Shire
Iohn Plantaginet Duke of Bedford
George Nevill Duke of Bedford
Iesper of Hatfield Duke of Bedford
PART OF HART FORD SHIRE
The Scale of Miles
1 2 3 4 5 6 7 8
S. Neot
Eynesbury
Berkford
Temsford
Tetworth
Everden
Coking Hatley
Potton
Sutton
Woumleghton
Sandye
Eworth
Tadlow
Bigleswade
Old werden
Duncott
Stratton
BIGGLESWAD
Edworth
Southhill
Shefford
Langford
HUNDR.
Astwick
Clyfton
Henlow
Arlesey
CLIFTON HU.
Stotfold
Mepsall
Holewell
Shillington
Baldok
Hicklingford
Higham Goben
Periton
Hitchin
Loulyc
Biscot
Walden
Luton
Summers
Merker
Talys Bridge
PASES
Ouse flu.

Felt Hats and Straw Bonnets

SOME parts of Britain have become well-known for their local products. The Luton area of Bedfordshire was once famous for its hats and bonnets and the local football team still rejoices under the name 'The Hatters' – but you would have to search in many shops today before you found a genuine Bedfordshire hat to wear!

Quite why the Luton and Dunstable area became so famous for the production of headgear is not really known, but its continued success was probably due to easy access to London. At one time the old Watling Street provided a straightforward route to the Metropolis, and later huge piles of hatboxes could be seen at Luton railway stations. At the peak of the hat industry, many thousands of people owed their living – either directly or indirectly – to the fashion for hats.

The business of making hats out of rushes and straw probably reached England in the 1300s, though the same ideas and materials had been used in other countries since prehistoric times. No-one really knows when the first straw hat was made in Bedfordshire, but we do know for certain that straw hats were being made in Dunstable in 1681. The town became the centre of a trade that was practised in hamlets and farmhouses throughout the surrounding district, with the finished products being brought to market in Dunstable. No doubt many of the hats were sold to travellers on Watling Street, but many more would have been sent to London.

By 1689 over a thousand families in the Luton and Dunstable district were said to depend on the straw hat trade for their livelihood, and there was concern that a law trying to force the wearing of woollen caps, to support the wool industry, would lead to pauperism and starvation. However, the trade survived and spread to encompass villages and towns throughout southern Bedfordshire, such as Toddington.

A local poet, Nicholas Rowe of Little Barford, was amused at the way Bedfordshire folk 'used their heads' to make a living. He wrote *A Poetical Address to the Ladies of Bedfordshire,* which included some lines about the straw hat trade:

> 'Thus trade increases, the poor are daily fed
> And thousands get their living by the head.'

Dunstable prospered and local people tried to expand the trade by using their skills in new directions. Instead of making just hats from straw, they turned out boxes, toys and even marquetry. Baskets, of course, were another useful branch of the trade but the decorated straw boxes proved to be subject to the vagaries of fashion – by 1859 Dunstable folk were limited to producing table mats and other minor oddments.

'Dunstable Bonnets' became well-known during the later years of the 18th century, though many of them were not made in Dunstable at all but simply taken there to be sold. During the time of the Napoleonic Wars bonnet making was a useful way of providing work for local paupers, and thus helping to keep down the Poor Rates. The trade spread as far north as Ampthill.

There is also a strong connection between the Napoleonic Wars and a man who became famous for his involvement with the straw-plait industry – Thomas Waller. Waller became one of the best-known leaders of the plait industry, but was not always popular; for a time he used to go to Yaxley Barracks, where French prisoners were kept, to buy plait from them. This was done illegally, since the low prices Waller could pay the French threatened the well-being of Bedfordshire's own plaiters.

The Waller initiative was followed by that of others – for example the Vyse factory opened in 1826 and the plaiting industry enjoyed a boom period in Luton, Dunstable and St Albans. It was given a boost by the existence of tariffs on imports of foreign-made plait, but with the popularity of Free Trade this protection was lost in 1842. Despite this, the plaiting industry dominated the south Bedfordshire economy during the mid 1800s.

By 1851 something like 10,000 people were employed in the trade, many of them women and children who worked at home. Some processes were so simple that young children could learn them and six year olds in Dunstable were said to be earning two shillings a week. This led to the setting up of the infamous 'plaiting schools', where large numbers of children divided their time between plaiting and education – or were meant to. In fact, of course, the 'schools' were really overcrowded cottages where small children were taught plaiting in order to earn money for their parents, while the 'teacher' was often as uneducated as the children themselves!

Gradually the law began to catch up with these plaiting schools. The Workshops Regulation Act of 1867 banned the employment of children under the age of eight altogether, and those between eight and 13 were only meant to work if they had ten hours at school per week. In 1871 a test case was brought against John Parrott, who ran a plaiting school at Leighton Buzzard. Parrott lost the case, and was ordered to close down his operation. Yet the schools survived until 1875 when the new laws on compulsory school attendance began to bite: the Luton School Board brought a prosecution for non-attendance, and the plaiting schools finally had to give way.

The plait was taken from the various villages to the special plait markets at Luton, Dunstable, Shefford and Toddington. Luton opened a Plait Hall in 1869, soon followed by Dunstable and Hitchin. There were some sharp practices among the traders, such as starting to trade at 2 am in order to catch the best prices! This was known as 'forestalling'.

With the improvement of sea transport, the Bedfordshire plaiters found their prices being undercut by imports from China and Japan from the 1870s. By 1914 the industry was in a sorry state and only a few plaiters were still working. The last plait was made at Offley in 1936.

This left the hat trade, which was largely dependent on straw bonnets and, later, felt hats. In the straw bonnet trade Dunstable led the way for quality, though Luton had a good share of the lower end of the market. The problem with this trade was, though, that it was highly seasonal. There could be little to do for much of the year, and then an urgent rush involving shifts of twelve hours or more. Nonetheless the trade had considerable value – Luton's cheap bonnets were worth £1.6 million in 1885.

The felt hat trade was rather slow to take off, since they were being made in the area from the 1870s but did not really become fashionable until after the First World War. By 1939 these felt hats accounted for three-quarters of Luton's hat and bonnet trade, but again this meant that the industry depended too much on the whims of fashion-conscious women, who could not be expected to go on buying hats in order to support the workers of Luton. The hat trade stopped in Dunstable in 1931 but continued in Luton until after the Second World War.

In the light of this the Luton Chamber of Commerce and the Borough Council showed exceptional wisdom in working together to attract other industries to the town. In 1905 they persuaded the Vauxhall Iron Works to move its new motor-car works out of London to Bedfordshire, followed by the Commercial Car Company the following year. By 1914 they had established an engineering presence in the town that was to become the basis of its prosperity in the 20th century in the way that hats and plait had been in the 19th. Perhaps it is time the Luton Town football team changed its nickname to something more appropriate?

The Arlesey Tragedy

IN December 1876 the name of the small Bedfordshire village of Arlesey hit the headlines for the worst of all reasons – it was the scene of one of those sudden and inexplicable disasters that seem to occur so often in the few days before Christmas. On Saturday 23rd December, thousands of people were going home for the festive season, or making their way to the welcoming houses of relatives, by way of the Great Northern Railway; few of them would have even realised that their journey took them through insignificant Arlesey, but it was at this Bedfordshire siding that fate struck a bitter blow.

Arlesey itself lay five miles north of Hitchin, at the end of a gentle decline that the northbound expresses used to pick up speed. Trains commonly passed Hitchin at about 50mph in 1876, picking up speed to a spritely 60 as they whistled past Cadwell signalbox and then over the points at Arlesey siding, one mile south of Arlesey station itself.

It was at Arlesey siding that tragedy was to strike. At about 3.30 pm on Saturday, 23rd December, a southbound goods train arrived at the siding from Peterborough. Its driver had charge of 25 trucks, but standing on the southbound track he needed to shunt across the northbound 'down' line in order to collect some goods wagons in the siding on the west side of the line. With a series of holiday expresses due, this could have been a hazardous manoeuvre, but signalman Graves was well used to the procedures.

Graves knew that the 2.45 pm express from Kings Cross to Manchester was due soon, but he had received no notification of it from the signalman at Cadwell. In any case, the points and signals at Arlesey siding were interlocked, so if the goods train shunted across the 'up' line it would automatically be protected by danger signals against the express.

All was conducted according to the regulations of the Great Northern Railway, but at 3.40 pm Graves received an urgent warning at his signalbox. 'The goods is derailed at the points!' a porter shouted to him, and Graves immediately thought of the approaching express. He telegraphed Cadwell signalbox, two and a quarter miles away, hoping to stop the express there, but it was too late. Graves thrust a red flag into the hand of the porter and told him to run down the line as an added warning to the express driver, but in the sleet and gloom it was unlikely the express would see the man in time.

As the goods had been shunting across the 'down' a truck of coprolites had become derailed on the points, dragging two other trucks off the track as well. The stationmaster at Arlesey siding, Walters, immediately called on some platelayers who were working nearby to come and help get the trucks back on the rails using the only thing available – brute force. They had hardly begun their efforts when they heard the distant roar of the approaching express.

The 2.45 pm was being driven by Driver Pepper, with 25 years experience, assisted by Stoker Smith. In the sleet and drizzle, with a heavy load, they had lost time on the climb out of London, but after Hitchin picked up speed rapidly to at least 60mph. After passing Cadwell signalbox, with all the signals at clear, Pepper must have sighted the danger signals ahead, for a man in a nearby field heard the engine whistling frantically – this was the signal for the guards in the train to apply the brakes in their vans.

On the slippery rails the train was going far too fast, and

had too little brake power, to stop. From the down distant signal to the derailed trucks was only 898 yards, yet the Great Northern's locomotive engineer later estimated the train would have needed 1,200 yards to stop with full brakes applied. Pepper seems only to have managed to slow it to about 35mph.

With collision inevitable, Stoker Smith leapt from the footplate of the speeding locomotive. A porter saw Smith 'topple over two or three times head foremost' and Smith soon died. Mrs Walters saw Pepper jump off, and watched helplessly as he landed on his head in her garden, suffering fatal injuries.

The express ploughed on and smashed into the goods trucks. Part of the locomotive cleared the wagons and landed on the track beyond, but it left its 'bogie frame' behind. The first six carriages of the lengthy train survived more or less intact, but the lack of continuous brakes caused some of the later carriages to concertina into each other and it was at this point that the three other deaths occurred. The immediate aftermath of the crash was an eerie silence:

> 'For a moment all was hushed and terror pervaded the minds of all present. But presently there arose from underneath the ruined carriages the cries of the wounded and imprisoned passengers'.

Fortunately a number of GNR officials were soon on the scene, one of whom ran along the line towards Cadwell in case following expresses ran into the wreckage. In fact the next express was warned by the signals at Cadwell, yet also failed to stop before it reached the 'home' signal – this time without causing an accident.

A crowd of uninjured and semi-hysterical passengers immediately assumed that the disaster had been caused by a signalling error and tried to invade the signalbox, but they were held back by Great Northern officials. Messengers were sent to Biggleswade for medical help, while five bodies were taken to the stables of the Lamb inn. Meanwhile the Great Northern continued to despatch holiday expresses from Kings Cross, until a queue of 14 had built up. Permanent way gangs managed to make a temporary connection by 10 pm so that the Christmas traffic could be restarted.

Two separate but parallel enquiries were begun into the accident – one by the coroner and another by Captain Tyler for the Board of Trade. Tyler began his enquiry on Christmas Day at Hitchin station, questioning all surviving personnel diligently.

The question as to whether Pepper had seen the signals and applied his brakes was soon solved. Guard William Thacker said he had heard the driver whistle for brakes and had applied his, while there was plenty of evidence that Pepper had shut off steam on the engine. However, one of the other guards believed that Pepper had not signalled for brakes until they had passed the distant signal.

In the case of such accidents, suspicion usually focussed on neglect of regulations by a signalman, but Graves was a calm and clear witness who proved that he had acted in accordance with the rules of the GNR which were, in any event, changed within a day or two of the accident. Graves said that he had known empty or goods trains to overrun signals, but never a passenger train – yet on 23rd December two successive expresses had both failed to stop within the limits of the signals.

Patrick Stirling, the Locomotive Superintendent, said that Pepper was not a drinker. He had been a driver since 1853 and had earned 44 premiums for good conduct.

Tyler read out his report into the causes of the accident at the coroner's court. He said that one of the causes had been excessive speed, noting that the collision had occurred 283 yards beyond the signal at which the train was meant to have stopped. However, he reported that the trains did not have sufficient brake power and that drivers were encouraged to keep to schedules even in difficult conditions. He commented on the failure of the following train to stop properly at Cadwell. But Tyler placed greater blame on the shunting regulations of the Great Northern and on the company's failure to instal continuous brakes in the trains – which had led to the deaths of the passengers in the middle carriages.

The coroner's jury then retired to discuss their verdict, and reported that the accident was the fault of Pepper, who had been neglectful, and the inefficiencies of the block signalling system. This verdict enraged the *Bedfordshire Times,* who felt it was unfair to lay the blame on two dead men when so many senior officials had neglected their responsibilities. It argued that the two dead men 'were forfeited to the defective arrangements of a rich Railway Company' and said the verdict was 'not less astonishing than lamentable' as well as 'sycophantic'.

There was certainly a good deal of criticism of the GNR – the length of the signalling blocks was inadequate for the speed of the trains and it had plainly changed its rules after the crash in recognition of their inadequacies. There were also many complaints that the company had continued to take passengers' money at Kings Cross when it knew the line to the north was blocked. The name of Arlesey became, for a while, synonymous with an acrimonious tragedy until, gradually, the disaster of Christmas 1876 was forgotten as other, and worse, crashes hit the headlines.

FLITWICK
MEDICINAL SPRING
FLITW

Wonderful Water from Flitwick

FAMOUS spa towns can be found throughout England, some with beautiful architecture and noble hotels. Bath, Cheltenham, Buxton and the others all became well-known because of the supposed healing powers of the natural waters that bubbled to the surface there. However, few today realise that humble Flitwick was once just as famous, and that its waters were celebrated in august medical journals.

In the mid 1800s Flitwick had little to crow about. Trains thundered through its station on their way from St Pancras to northern cities, but few of the passengers would have noticed anything remarkable about the local scenery. Certainly it would have been a keen-sighted traveller who would have caught a glimpse of Flitwick Moor.

The word 'moor' usually conjures up visions of desolate upland wastes. Flitwick Moor was certainly a wasteland, but it was little more than 200 ft above sea-level and noted largely for its springs, peat and marsh. However, its fortunes began to turn when Henry Stevens, an impressively-bearded man and sometime 'bird-stuffer', came to live at a nearby house named The Folly in 1859.

Stevens took a long-term tenancy on the house and 22 acres of the neighbouring moor. Part of this land was good enough to be planted with fruit trees, but just over half was rough woodland with springs bubbling through the peaty soil.

For a long time Stevens took little or no interest in Flitwick Moor, but in about 1880 he became convinced that the spring water had medicinal properties. Perhaps he picked some of the ideas up from local tradition, for it was local people who first used to visit the springs to soak cloths in the water. These cloths would then be applied to sores and cancers, supposedly with beneficial effects. Stevens began bottling the water and selling it at twopence a time. It sold well in the vicinity, but he had trouble penetrating the London market which had many other waters to choose from. The key to success was to win medical support, and this Stevens pursued assiduously. In 1885 his Flitwick Water was sent to the meeting of the National Health Society and won several awards. In 1887 the Pharmaceutical Society read of its unique qualities, but Stevens' real success came after an 1891 article in *The Lancet.*

This august medical journal described the Flitwick product as 'Chalybeate Water', and reported that it oozed through a long fissure in the black peat at a steady 45 degrees fahrenheit. It contained iron deposits which could be precipitated, and was found to contain a high level of ferric oxide. The peat gave the water the colour of a pale sherry, but its taste was slightly acidic and *The Lancet* recommended that the water be mixed with lemonade for drinking. *The Lancet* felt that Flitwick water had excellent qualities and, unlike a number of other brands, did not cause constipation.

Armed with such learned medical support, Flitwick (or rather, Stevens) was ready to conquer the world. The first step was to set up a depot in London and to place advertisements in the national press. But also the sanctity of the springs had to be preserved, so Stevens had them fenced in. Then, just when his enterprise seemed poised for success, Stevens died in 1898.

The house and the water business was sold that October for £2,450. The purchaser was R.W. White & Co, the well known soft drinks firm. They formed the Flitwick Chalybeate Company and marketed Flitwick Water throughout the country; for a time it was used regularly in hospitals and could be bought in shops and at railway stations.

It must be admitted, though, that Flitwick Water was not really as natural as it was claimed to be. Stevens used to dig up the peat, dry it for a year, and then filter the water through it to achieve the desired mineral content. His successors, under the control of Charles Short, continued this practice. They built a high fence round the spring and put a 60 ft shed over the top of the waters. The spring water was channelled into a filtering shed where bags of local peat were left to soak in the water so that it would absorb the iron content from it. The water, now with a peaty colour and extra mineral content, was then loaded into ten gallon jars and taken to the station.

Flitwick Water enjoyed its peak of popularity in the years between the death of Stevens and the start of the First World War. Advertisements for it that appeared about 1900 claimed that it had been a 'successful treatment' for consumption, rheumatism and various skin diseases. It was suggested that the water should be drunk in milk or beef tea and that businessmen should have a wineglass of it 'neat' one hour before dinner. Athletes and cyclists were advised to take two glasses a day.

The fashion for Flitwick Water did not last long and by 1930 demand was falling steadily. In 1938 the works closed down and the land was sold for farming, with most of the buildings being demolished. The other use for Flitwick Moor products survived a little longer – from 1910 to 1967 the peat was dug up for use in purifying the old town gas before North Sea gas was introduced. Now both uses of the moor are ended and there are few signs that Flitwick could once have been the spa of Bedfordshire.

Guy Fawkes Night

FOR most people in Victorian Bedfordshire, daily life was tough and unrewarding, and when tradition offered an excuse to release pent-up feelings they grasped the opportunity with enthusiasm.

The best example of this was the celebration of Guy Fawkes Night, which was an annual excuse for rowdy behaviour and heavy drinking. Then, as now, there were pranks with fireworks, but there were also occasions when law and order threatened to break down entirely. Because of this, not everyone enjoyed the celebrations; the *Bedfordshire Times* complained that 'stupid customs die hard, and the greater their absurdity the longer they live'. Its dour editor felt no joy in the celebration of an ancient tradition, complaining that Bedfordshire towns were given over to 'King Mob'.

The mid 1870s represented a turning point in Bedfordshire celebrations. Some towns still featured the old, rather anarchic and disorganised style of celebration, while other towns were trying to bring the events into some sort of decent order by holding organised carnivals and displays.

In 1876 there was, as usual, a Guy Fawkes procession through the centre of Bedford. This included the normal mixture of old-fashioned mummers, some torch and towball carriers and, more surprisingly, the local Fire Brigade. A good deal of alcohol had been drunk and spirits were high, so that a disregard for danger became apparent as the evening wore on.

This resulted in squibs and fire-crackers being thrown about, one of which was thrown through the open upstairs window of Mr Sheppard's florist's shop in the High Street.

Within seconds of the squib being thrown, Mr Sheppard's curtains had caught light and a real disaster seemed imminent. Mr Sheppard was away and the other people in the building failed to respond when some of the crowd knocked urgently at their door – perhaps they thought it was just drunks and troublemakers. The day was saved when a man named Stuart was hoisted up on the shoulders of the crowd, and managed to reach the burning window. He pulled down the curtains and threw them out into the street, then stamped out the flames that had spread to the carpet.

A peculiarity of Guy Fawkes Night in 1876 was that it was held on 6th November, the previous day being a Sunday and tradition keeping a sober respect for the Sabbath. Ampthill thus held its celebrations on Monday, and they were a lot better than Bedford's. A procession formed up at the Old Sun inn, and wove through the town led by a 'Guy', some torch carriers and the Ampthill Band, before climbing to Pinfold Hill. On the hilltop a crowd of over 2,000 people gathered to watch the lighting of a huge bonfire. There was an impressive firework display, with 'fireballs', rockets and Catherine Wheels. Some of the local lads brought a few noisy fireworks in their pockets, and these were thrown in among the ladies at various stages of the evening, causing 'much havoc' it was reported.

Biggleswade also favoured the torchlight procession idea, and even had the local brass band seated in an 'illuminated car'. People gathered outside the Royal Oak at 8.15 pm, completely blocking the streets. Two hundred young men appeared in a variety of grotesque costumes, carrying torches. Everyone then crowded along a route festooned with coloured lights to a big bonfire party in Clarke's Meadow near the river.

Even the smaller places tried to have some form of celebration. At Turvey, for example, the church bells were rung and hand crackers used. The whole district was marked by the glow of bonfires at isolated farms and hamlets.

The pressure from shopkeepers, local dignitaries and sober newspaper editors was for less excitement and much less drinking. The following year the celebrations in Bedford were very dull, except for a single incident when a man fired a pistol in the High Street – for which he was arrested.

At Biggleswade there was similar pressure to control the festivities. Sir John Burgoyne launched a campaign to persuade people to give money to the Indian Famine Relief Fund instead, but without much success. However, the Biggleswade Carnival Committee tried to make the event less spontaneous and improve its organisation. Not all went smoothly though, for the crowd that gathered by the Royal Oak had a long wait until anything happened – so they filled in time by throwing firecrackers about. The procession itself included some odd features – one of the floats depicted the execution of Mary Queen of Scots, which puzzled local reporters as to its connection with Guy Fawkes. Perhaps they had not read about Mary's Catholic plots to take over the English throne.

Mary was followed by a cart with Guy Fawkes on it, surrounded by clowns some of whom carried 'No Popery' banners. The procession included more young men in absurd costumes, and wound up in Clarke's Meadow again, where a balloon was sent up.

At Aspley Guise there was plenty of trouble before 5th November. On 2nd November a group of people set fire to a pile of wood outside Mr Yardley's house, then threw squibs against the windows. There was also trouble at Mr Steers' butcher's shop, where fireworks caused an 'explosion'. Despite fears, 5th November passed off peacefully enough except for the firing of a gun.

At Shefford 100 torch bearers gathered at the Bridge Foot inn for a procession led by the brass band. Despite police warnings, fireworks were let off in most of the streets. However, surely the final firework display was the most dangerous – for it was held from the arch of the railway bridge, with the crowd gathered in the road below. One wonders if the Midland Railway knew about this!

No doubt the people of Ampthill would have been grateful for a visit from the Shefford band that year, since the Ampthill Drum and Fife Band had lost its drums! To be more accurate, they had lent them to a Mr Butcher who had refused to return them, so dampening the town's Guy Fawkes celebrations.

Dunstable turned Guy Fawkes Night into more of an historical pageant. Guys were made of assorted villains, not all of whom had connections with anti-Catholic tradition: Faust, Henry VIII, Philip of Spain and the Duke of Gloucester were all on display. A bonfire was lit opposite the Priory and fireworks let off in Victoria Park.

Apparently tradition was dying most slowly in Luton. There the celebrations usually went on all day; young men (and older ones, too) made their own Guys and demanded money or beer in a Lutonian version of the 'penny for the Guy' tradition. The normal practice in the evenings was to throw bags of flour and soot around. Given these circumstances it is easy to imagine that many Luton folk were not keen on 5th November, and in 1877 many shops and houses were locked to prevent those in search of money gaining entrance.

However, there was still trouble in Luton. Money or drink for the Guys was demanded in 'the foulest language' and many were too afraid to refuse to give cash. At about 3 pm four men 'in period dress' entered the Red Lion and demanded beer in very impolite ways. The landlady reluctantly gave them some, but they then went into the bar where they found a number of farmers enjoying a quiet pint. More beer was demanded, but a Hertfordshire farmer – Mr Tooley – refused. The young men were angry, and kicked Tooley in the leg before leaving. The farmer was made of stern stuff, though, and followed them up the street until they beat him with a stick. They were later arrested at another pub nearby.

Perhaps these events of the afternoon showed the bad face of the old Guy Fawkes traditions. In the evening, Luton tried to show the good face of the new ways by copying the ideas of Hitchin. A procession of nearly a thousand people wound through the town, with a variety of displays on carts. These included a number of historical scenes, including Stanley in Africa, Cleopatra's Needle, Cromwell and Charles II.

However, this was all very modest compared to what had happened in Luton in 1828. In that year the justices had tried to ban the use of fireworks altogether, and this provoked a mob to attack the house of a hat manufacturer called Richard Jones. Perhaps he had influenced the decision of the justices. The mob blackened their faces and surrounded his house armed with squibs and stones. When a blazing tar-barrel was rolled out, Jones decided to act and shots rang out from his house. After a battle, the tar-barrel was put out and a major disaster averted.

So the chaotic scenes of the traditional Bedfordshire Guy Fawkes Night were gradually 'municipalised'. In the name of law and order, drunken revelry and high spirits were replaced by organised entertainment.

The Tragedy of the R101

ONE of the most famous scenes in Bedfordshire is of the two massive airship hangars at Cardington, south-east of Bedford. Here the famous airship, the R101, was constructed – a creation that brought the rich and famous to Cardington, but which was to meet a tragic end.

England had unkind memories of airships, for during the First World War the Germans had used Zeppelins to bomb various towns and cities – though they suffered a number of spectacular losses. This led the British to experiment with airships themselves, but early attempts were bedevilled with problems. The ZR2, or R33, for example, was built at Howden in Yorkshire but crashed near Hull in 1921 with the loss of 44 lives.

The R38, built at Cardington, also met disaster; in fact there was a saying that 'no ship built at Cardington ever flies for long'. Cardington had been established as a wartime airship base and the aircraft firm of Shorts had been based there – hence the nearby village known as Shortstown. To build the air ships a huge shed, 700 ft long, had been set up at Cardington and, at the time, it was said to be the largest building in the world.

Despite these setbacks, the British government was anxious to press on with its policy of developing airships. In 1924 it

R 101
G-FAAW

decided to commission two machines – the R100 to be built at Howden to the design of Barnes Wallis, and the R101 to be built in the government base of Cardington. The teams building each of the airships soon developed a certain amount of competitive feeling, though this did not prove to be good for safety, especially as the Air Ministry refused to allow the use of more powerful but untried engines on the R101.

The R101 made its first flight in October 1929. It had to be eased out of the shed in calm weather to avoid damage, a task that employed the 200 men who worked at Cardington, 150 airmen from Henlow, and 50 unemployed men from Bedford. Everyone agreed that the R101 was a beautiful creation, but it lacked power and rose only sluggishly into the air; its huge bulk was held aloft by gas bags made of membranes from bullock intestines and filled with hydrogen.

The first flight, on 14th October 1929, was around Bedford but another trip was made over Sandringham to please King George V. On 17th November the R101 made a longer trip to Edinburgh and Dublin before returning to Cardington. However, there were clearly problems with the R101 and it was put back into the giant shed, cut in two, and a new bay inserted in the middle to give it more 'lift'. To accommodate the large size of the airship, the shed at Cardington had to be extended to 800 ft long, and its height was raised to 157ft; even so, the airship filled the shed to within a few inches of its ceiling.

It was brought out again in June 1930, but attempts to fly it on two successive days resulted in major tears in its covering. The very size of the airship meant that it was subject to enormous strain from the wind, although it was held together by 450,000 rivets.

The airship's first major flight was from Cardington to Hendon for the air show on 28th June 1930. On the return flight it suddenly pitched into a steep dive for 500 ft. The crew managed to bring the ship back under control, but then it ran into another dive and after that a third. A ton of water ballast had to be jettisoned to bring the R101 back to a steady course but when it got back to Cardington it was found that small holes had appeared in the hydrogen bags.

Meanwhile the R100 was making good progress and that summer it managed to fly across the Atlantic to Montreal, though there were a few scares on the way. It returned across the Atlantic to Cardington in a little over 57 hours.

The R101 was plainly not as safe as its privately constructed rival but Lord Thomson, the Secretary of State for Air, was keen to use it for a scheduled trip to India that September. Thomson, who had political ambitions in India, wanted to see a regular airship service from Cardington to Karachi, via Ismailia in Egypt. The R101 had a major problem with its fabric, which crumpled like scorched brown paper, but Thomson's pressure caused repairs to be hurried and the fabric was patched up using a rubber solution.

With Thomson insisting that he must leave on 4th October, the rebuilt R101 ventured out for a test flight on 1st October. At 777 ft long it was the largest airship in the world, and was an impressive spectacle. Thomson said that, 'the R101 was as safe as a house, except for the millionth chance'. Sadly for Thomson and the others who travelled with him, the chances were rather more heavily against the R101 than he supposed.

The airship left Cardington for the last time on 4th October 1930, at 6.36 pm. It carried 42 crew, six officials and six passengers. A crowd of over 3,000 came to watch the departure of the huge airship and they were, no doubt, impressed by talk of Cardington becoming 'the world's greatest airport' with regular services to India and beyond; it is doubtful that few of those watching knew that Thomson himself had prepared for the journey by writing a new will and taking out life insurance. But even the first few miles proved hazardous, for the airship had to dump four tons of its water ballast to compensate for the heavy load of passengers, baggage and fuel.

The weather was unsuitable for such a huge airship and over Hitchin she encountered strong winds. 'She's moving more like a sea-going ship than an aircraft', one man observed. The R101 was so low that it caused a Mrs Leslie to run away from her cottage in terror. Matters got worse, for there were also problems when an aft engine broke down. As the winds increased steadily, the huge and lumbering airship struggled over the Weald and south towards the coast at Hastings. Leaving England behind, the R101 was travelling at barely 700 ft above the waves and its First Officer adjusted the height to a safer 1,000 ft. Yet progress was still difficult, for winds of 35mph were now being experienced and these gave the vast flanks of the airship a considerable battering.

The passengers, though, seemed oblivious to the problems caused by the weather. Before retiring to bed they were allowed to smoke cigars – an obvious hazard in an airship held aloft by huge amounts of hydrogen.

At about 2 am the R101 passed over the French city of Beauvais, the sound of its engines waking many of the citizens since it was very low. Beyond the city the ground rose into a shallow ridge that would normally have posed no danger for air traffic, but by this time the R101 was desperate for every foot of altitude. At a crucial moment the airship shook into one of the fateful dips that had troubled it on the voyage back from Hendon. Attempts were made to steady it by cutting the speed of the engines, but the crew had simply too little altitude to play with.

The R101 did not so much crash into the ground as belly-flop along it. Its underparts scraped the surface of the ridge over a distance of about 60 ft before the greatest danger to all airships of the time engulfed it – the hydrogen caught fire.

The death of the R101 was witnessed by a French farmer, Eugene Rabouille. He reported that, 'There was at once a tremendous explosion, which knocked me down. Soon flames rose into the sky to a great height. Everything was enveloped by them. I saw human figures running about like madmen in the wreck. Then I lost my head and ran away into the woods'.

If the accident had occurred in daylight there may well have been fewer casualties, for the 'gondolas' that carried some of the passengers and crew actually hit the ground quite gently so that those who were alert were able to leap out before the horrifying fire ensnared them. However, many inside were asleep, and many of the civilian passengers were trapped in their beds.

A few managed to escape from the flames of the R101. Two men found themselves entirely surrounded by scorching heat and fierce flames, but the water from a fractured tank suddenly fell onto the flames around them. For a few seconds the heat was dowsed, and the men leapt out to safety.

Altogether 48 people died in the tragedy of the R101, the great airship that will for ever be associated with Bedfordshire. The accident was a fatal blow to all who had hoped that airships could prove a reliable means of international travel and one airship pioneer, Santos-Dumont, attempted to hang himself.

Yet after the tragedy the arguments still raged, for it was never agreed what had actually caused the crash of the R101. Some took the view that the stormy winds had torn a hole in the airship's 'envelope', causing the gas bags to leak so that it lost valuable height. Others believed that the huge strain put on the R101's frame by the storm had been too much, and that it had buckled under the pressure. Whatever the real reason, the idea of airships for passenger travel was dead and the more successful R100 was sold for scrap – its value being £450.

Many of the dead crew came from Shortstown and for a few days the village was plagued with journalists and 'well-wishers'. One widow was visited by some 'concerned' helpers, who stole her bicycle and a gold watch. In Bedford blinds were drawn in many houses and the Salvation Army played the Dead March over and over again. The bodies were brought back to Bedford by ship and train via Euston, with two flights of bomber aircraft passing over the town as the train drew in. The 48 coffins were then loaded onto lorries and taken to Cardington, though only 14 of the sombre wooden boxes had names on them. At Cardington they were all interred in a mass grave and the airship's flag, which had somehow survived the wreck, was placed in the church.

The last memorial of the R101 is not really the grave at Cardington, but the airship sheds that still dominate the

Bedfordshire countryside for miles around. Though nothing as spectacular as the R101 has ever been built there since, the sheds have found periodic use since airship technology was adapted for barrage and weather balloons. The sheds have even been used to provide an indoor arena for model aeroplane competitions. The shed at Karachi, never put to its original use, was accommodation for 3,000 men during the Second World War; one wonders how many of them knew of the link between this tragic and forlorn building and the similarly sad sheds at Cardington.

The Strange Affair of the Clapham Coffin

ON a dark October night in 1876, strange events were occurring in the churchyard of the small village of Clapham. A number of darkly-clothed men, with serious if not sinister expressions on their taut faces, gathered in small groups by the shelter of the church wall. It was a wet night, and the heavy clouds blotted out the light of the moon, seemingly so that dark deeds could be accomplished under the shield of blackness.

What was the sinister group doing in a churchyard at such an unearthly hour? Some of them carried spades, hinting that they might be 'resurrectionists' come to steal a corpse. It was just after one in the morning when some of the men with spades, shovels and crowbars advanced on the low iron railings that surrounded a large and imposing brick tomb. Above the brickwork was a large stone slab, and mounted on that was an imposing cross of marble. This was no common grave, and its inhabitant no Bedfordshire peasant – for the inmate was the deceased squire of Clapham, Reverend John Dawson.

Throughout the night the men worked on the tomb while some stood by, dressed in finer clothes, trying to see the time on their watches and muttering about the labourers who had failed to turn up to help in the task. 'This is no good', one of the men said, 'we won't be finished by daylight and then the villagers will turn up – poking their noses in and asking awkward questions'.

The man was right, for with a depleted workforce the 'resurrectionists' had hardly got the coffin out onto the grass of the churchyard before a large crowd had gathered. One or two villagers had been attracted by rumours that 'body-snatchers' were after the old squire, but the more sagacious of villagers knew that no medical man would pay good money for an eight year old corpse.

The morning light revealed that a few of the men by the church wall were police constables, one of whom clutched a warrant from the Home Secretary for the disinterment of Rev Dawson. As the crowd gathered, the police were called on to keep the inquisitive at a respectful distance.

Dawson's coffin had two layers and, as it was pulled out onto the grass, the bottom of the inner coffin gave way and deposited the corpse into the outer coffin as it lay on the ground. Some of the crowd stepped back a little at this, superstitious fear of the dead making them uneasy.

One of the dark-clothed gentlemen was a doctor from St Neots, and he set about examining the corpse with a professional detachment that the crowd could only wonder at. First he looked at the body of the old man, with its striking white hair 'as fresh-looking and bright as when the remains had been interred'. The body itself was also well-preserved, which the doctor decided was due to the coffin having been packed full of sawdust which had kept the body from decomposing. Also in the coffin, and rather sinister perhaps, were two soft felt hats and a black silk mantle.

The doctor tied a rope around the feet of the corpse and used it to gently raise the legs of the erstwhile Rev Dawson. As he did so, all the officials peered anxiously beneath them, as if expecting to find something hidden there. The doctor confirmed that nothing was hidden behind the legs and, at this news, the faces of the gentlemen were a mixture of pleasure and worry.

The doctor then moved around to the upper part of the body, and affixed his rope carefully around it. Gently he raised the shoulders and chest from their bed of sawdust. and then there was a sudden cry. 'There!' a young gentleman shouted, and an older man reached forward to snatch up a packet of papers. The crowd caught a brief glimpse of three or four bundles of what looked like letters, done up with red tape.

The gentlemen had found what they were looking for, and turned away. The old man had yielded up his last secret, and they showed no more interest in him. Only the doctor thought fit to muse upon the body's extraordinary state of preservation, which later merited a paragraph or two in the celebrated medical journal, *The Lancet.*

What was the cause of this unusual exhumation? Its origins, in fact, lay in a complex legal case that stretched back over several years and involved that favourite topic of the Victorians, the inheritance of property – in this case the manor and estates of Woodlands at Clapham.

The story can be traced back to John Dawson senior, who inherited some property in Yorkshire. In 1812 he sold this and used the proceeds to buy Woodlands. Dawson became well-known in Bedfordshire and was High Sheriff for a time. When he died the property passed to his son, Rev John Dawson.

The Rev Dawson married twice. By his first wife he had a son, William Henry Dawson, and a daughter. After his first wife died he married his housekeeper, Miss Proctor, which would have been a fairly shocking thing in those times of class consciousness. The second Mrs Dawson also had a son and a daughter.

When Rev Dawson died his will caused something of a surprise, for he left the property to his son by the second marriage and only an annuity of £200 to his elder son. This may have seemed a surprising course of action to many, but there seems to have been good reason for it. William Dawson had been a very frail child and was not expected to live to maturity, so he had been kept at home and not educated in the normal way. As he got older and seemed likely to survive, his father adopted the view that the boy would not need an education as he would naturally succeed to the property and draw his income from it. In fact it must have gradually dawned upon the Rev Dawson that all was not right with his oldest son, for the boy did not learn to read until he was past 20 years old, and tended to have a naive trust in all and sundry.

Under such circumstances as these, Rev Dawson must have decided that William would be incapable of looking after the estate and would be safer with a guaranteed annual income. He therefore left the estate to his younger son when he died in October 1870.

Naturally, William felt aggrieved by this and he retired to the Isle of Wight. His story was, however, well known in the Bedford district and became the subject of rumour. A common story was that Rev Dawson had actually made another will – a will of entail – which would have given his elder son first rights to the property. This version was supported by the rector of Bletsoe, among others, but there was no documentary proof.

At this point the figure of Alfred Nicholson enters the story. Nicholson was a Bedford solicitor, though not one who emerges with any credit from the tale. Perhaps he had been reading Dickens' *Bleak House* and knew that the legal profession could make a great deal of money out of disputed inheritances, but he somehow 'happened to meet' William Dawson in the Isle of Wight during 1872. The two got talking about the Woodlands estate and Nicholson persuaded Dawson to let him bring an action – there was a complicated plan about how this was to be financed and how costs or spoils were to be divided.

Dawson's cousin, Wade-Gery of St Neots, advised him that it was hopeless to try and fight the case, but William Dawson seems to have had no faith in anyone but the wily Nicholson. As a first step, Dawson and Nicholson brought an action in July 1872 for the eviction of George Ballingall from Rookery Farm on the estate. Ballingall had rented the farm from the second son of Rev Dawson. William Dawson's case depended entirely on the existence of a will of entail, but this could not be proved; the judge ruled against him and he had to bear the costs of £135.

This seems to have soured the relationship between William Dawson and Nicholson, so that by 1875 the latter was suing the former. Dawson's hopes to rescue something from the case rested upon the evidence of a carpenter from Gwyn Street, Bedford, named Maxey. The carpenter said that Rev Dawson's first mother-in-law, who had nursed him through his illness, had placed a packet in the coffin before Maxey had screwed the lid on for what he had assumed to be the last time. Dawson believed that the will of entail was contained among these documents.

Representatives of William Dawson then applied to the Home Secretary for permission to exhume the body in search of the will, and this was granted. Thus the strange events of Clapham churchyard came to take place.

So what was hidden in the coffin? The papers found there were stained, shrunk and decayed. They were incapable of being opened out without causing them damage, despite the efforts of Dr Lyon of Bedford. In any event they were of little use to William Dawson, for they were mostly love letters between his father and his mother. So the case lapsed – for though there were several people who claimed to know there was another will, no-one could find it, and Rev Dawson took his secrets back into the grave with him.

God's Highwayman

THE pages of the *Newgate Calendar* are full of rogues who committed terrible crimes and ended their days swinging from a rope at Tyburn or in the rat-infested dungeons of Newgate Gaol itself. It is something of a surprise, therefore, to find the name of a Bedford citizen in its pages and, moreover, a citizen who claimed to be inspired in his crimes by God!

Jacob Halsey was born into a wealthy Bedford Quaker family in the middle of the 17th century. He was educated at Bedford Grammar School and seemed to have made an excellent start in life. However, he used to love playing near the river and one day was pushed in; he was rescued by a bargee, but some believe the shock of this experience permanently affected Halsey's mind.

His father certainly had trouble guiding him along the path mapped out for him. In 1666 Jacob's father tried to make him into a farmer, but he upset all the labourers by trying to convert them to Quakerism. Halsey was deeply religious and told the labourers about the numerous visions he had had. During what was left of his spare time, Halsey loved nothing more than to go into Bedford and preach.

Halsey's religious enthusiasms opened him up to a fair amount of ridicule, but he also seems to have been rather gullible. One night, after Halsey had gone to bed, a local rogue crept up outside his window and called up, 'Jacob, where art thou?' Jacob woke up and thought that he was hearing the call

REPENT YE

of God, so he answered accordingly. 'Arise presently, Jacob my beloved', the voice continued, 'and go to the church, or rather steeple-house, and break all the windows'.

Believing himself under divine instruction, and doubtless thinking that God would share his own antipathy to vanities such as stained glass windows, Halsey went to a nearby church and smashed its windows with a pole. For this he was arrested, spent three months in prison and had to pay costs of £400.

Such was Halsey's commitment to evangelism, that he doubtless saw time in prison as a chance to preach to the wicked. In fact the reverse occurred, for it was the prisoners who preached to and converted Halsey. They told him all about their illegal activities and caught his imagination with tales of a gang called The Plumers, on account of their wearing plumed hats. This gang would deliberately start quarrels in the street in order to cover up their pickpocketing exercises, and at night would cheat the gentry at various games.

When he was released from prison, Halsey found life in Bedford virtually intolerable. Everyone knew of how he had been made a fool of about the church windows, and he was jeered at in the street. Children followed him around, laughing and crowing. What he had heard in prison now proved an inspiration to Halsey – he would become a highwayman.

He threw away his plain Quaker garb and equipped himself with a suitable outfit for a highwayman – a wig, a cocked hat, strident neckcloth and a fashionable coat. One of his first known victims was an unscrupulous money-lender that he met on the road between Barnet and St Albans. Halsey rode along with the man for a few miles, and then declared himself a highwayman.

'Lend what thou hast, without any grumbling', he demanded, but this was a bargain the money-lender was reluctant to agree to. When the usurer resisted, Halsey shot his horse from under him. He stole £60 and tied the man to an elm tree, but in an open enough position that he would be rescued by a passer-by.

Halsey then set out on a life of crime, robbing many on the roads around London. He never knowingly robbed a Quaker, and often lectured his victims on the benefits of Quakerism. On another occasion he robbed a country curate on the road between Abingdon and Oxford, giving Halsey a chance to complain about the Established Church's practice of demanding tithes. 'Deliver thy mammon to the righteous,' Halsey shouted, 'that he may convert it to a better use than to exhaust it in gluttony and pride, otherwise I will send thee to the bottomless pit before thy time is come by the course of nature'. Halsey had no doubts about the eternal destination of Anglican clergymen! He got away with £32.

Halsey then transferred his operations to Kent, where he made a fatal mistake. In 1691 he stopped the Earl of Westmorland near Wateringbury, but such a man as the Earl was unlikely to travel without protection. Halsey was seized by the earl's men and taken to the gaol in Maidstone.

He was tried in Maidstone although he pleaded to be sent back to Bedford for judgement. There was no doubt about Halsey's guilt and he was sentenced to death. He was hanged in April 1691 in Maidstone, with the unexceptional but calm last words of 'I bid ye all farewell'.

The Robber Baron

MANY hundreds of years ago England was an unhappy land. During the Crusades, King Richard had left the country with the result that anarchy and wickedness flourished. When his brother, King John, took over there were all the signs that the country would pass from a bad state into one even worse. Nowhere had fared worse in those troubled times than Bedfordshire, it seemed. The traditional protectors of the county were the de Beauchamps family, who had held Bedford Castle since the days of the Norman Conquest. Yet even the de Beauchamps family had fallen on hard times, for the lord of Bedford Castle had been thrown out and the fortress entrusted to one of John's henchmen, Sir Fulke (or Fawkes) de Breaute.

Sir Fulke became feared throughout the surrounding area. He even burst upon the town of St Albans at the head of a raiding party. Sir Fulke ransacked the town and then turned his attention to the Abbey, which had riches and treasures of its own. The Abbey's bailiff had tried to turn the robbers aside, but he had been struck down with a mortal blow.

On a cold January day shortly afterwards, a young knight of the de Beauchamps family, Ralph, was riding sadly through the county that he might once have looked upon as his natural inheritance. Ralph was the nephew of the broken nobleman who had lost Bedford to Sir Fulke and, though he was a brave young man, he lacked the status and resources that would have fallen to the heir of a grand estate.

Ralph was on his way to the de Pateshulle family manor at Bletsoe, but he was no longer the welcome guest that he once would have been. Aliva, his sweetheart, was a beautiful young girl from a respectable gentry family, and her father no longer considered the penniless young knight a suitable match for her. Ralph arrived at the manor without de Pateshulle knowing, and was able to snatch a few moments with Aliva without her father's consent. During this short time Aliva told Ralph that her father planned to marry her to William de Breaute, the younger brother of the wicked Sir Fulke. Ralph was shocked to hear this, and left Bletsoe with a heavy heart.

William de Breaute rode into Bletsoe that afternoon confident of winning the hand of the fair Aliva. Though he was party to many of his older brother's schemes, he had not been involved in the raid on St Albans. Aliva, though, knew something of his reputation and had heard the reports of the activities of his family. When he was led into her presence she did indeed offer him her hand – as a slap across the face. William turned about and left Bletsoe in a fury, his passion for the girl only increased by this curt refusal of what he assumed was a blameless proposal of marriage.

Sir Fulke was a man of the world, and he understood clearly that he had made a mistake in attacking the Abbey. He realised that even the King would not approve and decided to try and make amends. He rode to St Albans in plain, simple clothes, leaving his weapons behind. To the astonishment of the monks, he pleaded penitence before the Abbot and asked how he could make amends for his wickedness. Fulke was not prepared to pay for forgiveness, but he agreed to be disciplined and scourged with knotted cords as Henry II had been after the death of Becket.

One can question the sincerity of Sir Fulke in visiting St Albans, especially since there were rumours that the King was about to start a legal inquiry into his activities. In fact three justices had already begun to take steps to curb Sir Fulke's power, so the robber baron began to plot with his brother William to have the three kidnapped. William's interest was quickened when he learnt that one of the three was Martin de Pateshulle, uncle of the girl who had spurned him so cruelly. William had also learnt that Aliva loved the penniless Ralph de Beauchamps, and his heart was full of hatred for the handsome young knight.

Two of the justices, Thomas de Muleton and Henry de Braybrooke, were heading south towards Dunstable via Turvey. This was a slow journey on horseback in those days, and the justices had arranged to meet Martin de Pateshulle at Rougemont Castle. They never got there, for William de Breaute ambushed them near Eversholt. In the struggle that took place, de Braybrooke was captured by the de Breaute henchmen, but Thomas de Muleton escaped and managed to reach Rougement. William was furious when he discovered he had caught only one of the three justices.

With the one prize that he did have, William began the return journey to Bedford at a gallop. His men raced through Elstow at just the moment that Aliva and her Uncle Martin were leaving the priory where she had been in retreat. The two groups virtually collided in the road, and Martin de Pateshulle was knocked off his horse without being recognised as one of the men who was being sought.

William, though, could hardly fail to spot Aliva, and in an instant conceived the plan to kidnap her too. Aliva realised that her only chance was to ride straight for Bletsoe where she could expect at least a degree of protection. She turned her horse towards the bridge at Bromham, but this was not an easy ride as much of the route lay across the marshes and water meadows along the broad valley of the Ouse.

It was a long struggle for Aliva but ultimately her superior local knowledge saved her from the wicked clutches of the de Breaute men. At last Aliva's horse could carry her no further, so she wandered through Bromham looking for some place of shelter. Her heart naturally turned to the merciful power of the

Holy Church and when she saw the chapel at Bromham bridge, she decided to seek sanctuary within. As she slipped inside she was watched by Brother Bertram, the Bromham priest, who had left an order of monks under very doubtful circumstances.

Some hours later William de Breaute and his men rode up to the bridge at Bromham. They had realised that Aliva would have headed this way in order to reach her father's estates, so they began to question villagers in the hope of learning of her movements. The villagers had no reason to love the de Breaute family and all, in traditional manner, claimed to have seen nothing.

It was then that the priest of Bromham, Brother Bertram, sidled up to William with a knowing grin upon his greedy face. 'I know where the young lady you seek can be found', he said, clearly indicating by one or two mercenary gestures that his knowledge could only be acquired for a suitable consideration. The priest haggled over a price, then assured William that he should watch and wait for his opportunity. With the priest's connivance, Aliva was captured and carried out of the chapel and off to Bedford Castle.

As soon as he heard the news, Ralph saddled his horse and rode at full speed to Bedford. There he found only frustration, for the drawbridge had been raised and, a lone knight, he could do little to attack the castle. 'Where is Aliva?' Ralph shouted at the stark castle battlements, but his only reward was to see Sir Fulke and William laughing down at him. Sir Fulke turned aside to speak with one of his guards; seconds later, the guard let fly a bolt from his crossbow and it struck Ralph. Fulke and William laughed as some Bedford people came forward to carry the wounded knight to safety.

All this left poor Aliva in a desperate situation. Her champion was wounded, possibly even dying, and there seemed no-one with the power to rescue her. Fortunately she succeeded in befriending Beatrice Mertoun, companion to the wife of Sir Fulke, Lady Margaret.

In fact there was more hope for Aliva than she could realise while locked up in the security of Bedford Castle. King John had died in 1216, but Sir Fulke de Breaute had carried on as if his protector was still alive. It gradually became clear to Henry III and his advisers that Sir Fulke was a major threat to the stability of the kingdom, though this must have been a difficult decision to take as many could still remember Sir Fulke's valiant efforts in the victorious struggle against the French at Lincoln in 1217. But Sir Fulke had gone too far by kidnapping one of the King's own justices, and it was clear that the King would have to act against Bedford Castle, the seat of the de Breaute power.

To do this, a good siege engineer was required – and so John de Standen, sweetheart of Beatrice Mertoun, was summoned to the King at Northampton. If the castle was to be captured, knowledge of its defences was needed too and a member of the disaffected de Beauchamps family would be valuable. So it was that Ralph was sent for and, at Northampton, he explained to John de Standen the secrets of the castle in which he had grown up.

On 22nd June 1224 the King arrived in Bedford at the head of a large army, but one of the birds had flown. Sir Fulke had escaped to Wales, leaving his brother William in charge of defending Bedford Castle against impossible odds. Many came to Bedford to share in the work, for there were thousands who hoped to see the end of the dreaded de Breaute clan.

John de Standen's men laboured for days and at last there was a success as the King's men were able to advance and capture the outer defences of the castle. This, though, was barely the beginning, for there was still the Old Tower to capture before the King's men could advance on the keep. The siege engineers began their work once more, burrowing deep under the Old Tower. One day, when the work was nearly complete, de Standen took his friend Ralph down into the dark tunnel. They stood silently together, marvelling that they were under the very cellars of the Old Tower. Silence was essential, for any sound could betray the presence of the tunnel to the defenders. As the two men stood there, they heard the clear voices of two young women and both male hearts leapt with joy – for these were the voices of Aliva and Beatrice! They were so close, and yet so far apart.

The next day the tunnels beneath the Old Tower were set alight and its walls came crumbling down. Ralph led the surge of men into the attack and pressed on to where William de Breaute himself was fighting. William threw himself with desperation at his old enemy and it seemed that Ralph would be killed. Yet, just as William's sword was poised to strike the fatal blow, a monk pushed across and deflected his blow away from Ralph. Furious, William turned his attention to the unarmed Benedictine monk and killed him with a single blow.

The monk had diverted William's attention, giving Ralph time to recover. He moved into the attack once more, this time more cautiously but with deadly intent, but William evaded his blows and escaped to the keep.

William and the last of the defenders fought on, for they knew that they could expect no quarter from the King. Instead John de Standen had to begin his mining again, this time digging beneath the keep in which Beatrice and Aliva were still imprisoned. On 14th August, with the collapse of the keep imminent, its last defenders surrendered to Lord Lisle of Rougemont. Ralph immediately rushed into the building, fearing that the ladies had been subjected to some awful fate, but he found them at last on the actual roof of the keep where they had fled to escape the fire and the fighting.

William and 73 of the castle's garrison were arrested and hanged outside its walls. Three of the de Breaute knights, however, pledged themselves to take the Cross and join the Crusades, so they were cut down while still alive. The fate of the others served as an awful reminder of the perils of rebelling against the King.

John de Standen was ordered by the King to destroy the castle so that it would never again be a source of trouble, after which he married his beloved Beatrice in the chapel at Bedford bridge. Aliva, of course, married her long-suffering Ralph who was now the heir to the de Beauchamps' estate once more.

Thus ends the tale of the Robber Baron of Bedford Castle. Like all romantic stories, this one has grown in the telling; perhaps it was because of this that the story of the Robber Baron was so popular in Victorian times, and deserves its revival today.

The Forgotten Aviator

WHEN the great names of early aviation history are discussed, people tend to mention the Wright brothers, Louis Bleriot, Alcock and Brown and a few others. Bedfordshire's Grahame White is largely forgotten, despite the fact that he was an undoubtedly brave aviation pioneer, for he never managed to do anything *first*.

Grahame White was a Bedford boy who attended the local grammar school, but Latin and Shakespeare did not interest him half as much as anything mechanical. Whilst still living in Bedford he became well-known as a dashing rider of a motorcycle, but he soon abandoned two wheels for four and became just as daring as a car driver. He must, though, have proved that he was equally as capable of driving carefully, as he was appointed chauffeur to His Majesty the King for a while.

So far White's interests had remained resolutely on the ground, but in 1909 he attended the famous air show at Rheims in France and was captivated by the new flying machines. He wheedled his way into the confidence of a famous French expert, Farman, who was impressed by White's coolness under pressure. Late in 1909 White learnt to fly using an old Bleriot plane.

At about this time the *Daily Mail* announced a competition for the first person to fly from London to Manchester, with a prize of £10,000. The rules were simple – you were allowed to stop on the way, but the journey must be completed within 24 hours. White saw this as his chance for fame and glory, and persuaded Farman to design and build a plane for him. The plane was built in Britain, but Farman came over before the race to check that it was satisfactory.

White was in a hurry to start since he had heard that another Frenchman, Monsieur Paulhan, had entered the race too. In April 1910 he decided to make his bid for the prize, and set out from Park Royal at 5.15 am. White flew over Wormwood Scrubs in order to come close enough to central London to qualify for the rules, then turned north-west to follow the London & North-Western Railway line as far as Rugby.

White's plane reached Rugby in a creditable 83 minutes, but he was having problems with the intense cold and a rising wind that made the fragile craft dangerous. He landed at Rugby for a rest and then planned to make the next stage to Crewe, but as he flew over Lichfield the cold and the wind became too much and so he landed – only 69 miles from Manchester.

White hoped that the weather would improve overnight, leaving him plenty of time to complete the journey to Manchester within the 24 hours stipulated, but it did not. So, it seemed, his chance of glory had been snatched from his grasp.

Undaunted, White decided to return to London and try again, but by this time Paulhan was nearly ready to make his own flight. Just after returning to London, White was standing in his hotel lobby talking to reporters when he suddenly received the news that Paulhan had taken off. There was no time to lose! Though he was not properly prepared, White rushed to his plane and took it up into the air again.

Paulhan had made a good start and the weather seemed satisfactory. He flew straight over Rugby and did not stop, his plane watched by large crowds that had already heard that there was a race between the two air aces. Paulhan landed at Lichfield for a break, then climbed back into the skies for a final and successful run to Manchester.

So where was Grahame White, Bedfordshire's ace pilot? He had been delayed by the need to prepare his plane, and it had been nearly dusk before he took off. He followed the same railway line towards Rugby, but was increasingly battered by a rising wind. The railway junction at Roade confused him, and he followed the line to Northampton before realising his mistake and turning back. After stopping at Roade, he restarted for Manchester but was forced by weather and exhaustion to land at Polesworth near Tamworth.

Paulhan claimed the £10,000 prize and poor White slipped quietly into the footnotes of aviation history.

A Week in Old Bedfordshire

WHAT was life like in Bedfordshire in the 19th century? Let us follow through a week in the county's life in 1891, a week that straddled the end of November and the start of December. It was in no way an exceptional week, so it is a good example of Bedfordshire life as it was then.

At the time there was only one major scandal that was interesting the people of the county, which focused on what was then a very thorny issue – education. Education was not a political issue as it is now, but a religious issue, and the various church organisations lost no opportunity to complain about how the others ran their schools. The scandal that had attracted most attention was a result of the death by drowning of a Sandy schoolboy a few weeks earlier; the coroner had ruled that the boy committed suicide and it was believed by some that this was due to harsh treatment by the headmaster at his Church of England school. Some nonconformists seem to have relished the chance to annoy the Anglicans, and local newspaper editors had to wade through prolonged correspondence on the subject.

Thursday 26th November saw activity in the courtroom at Ampthill. A tramp was brought in for breaking windows at a beerhouse, and also for tearing up his clothes while in custody. He was given three months hard labour. The main cultural event in Bedford that day was an appearance of the D'Oyly Carte Opera Company, performing *The Mikado* at the Corn Exchange.

The main event in the county on Friday 27th November was the funeral of Charles Magniac, a local dignitary. Magniac was a very wealthy man, his fortune being based upon his father's role in the firm of Jardine, Matheson & Co. Magniac died in London on the previous Monday, but was brought home to Sharnbrook for burial – he lived at Colworth House. A special train was run from Bedford to Sharnbrook so that many local gentry could attend the funeral, at which Magniac's hearse was followed by his favourite horse and dog.

The evening of Friday 27th November was a chance for some to relax. In Blunham a 'musical entertainment' was provided in the schoolroom, which concluded with a 'laughable sketch' called 'The Black Schoolmaster'.

On the morning of Saturday 28th November at about 8 am a newborn child died at Cranfield. The child was illegitimate and its death might have attracted suspicion but for the fact that the nurse was present at the time. The mother was in bed with the child lying at her side when the nurse brought her a cup of tea. As the mother turned to take the cup, the baby seems to have rolled over behind her and was found suffocated shortly afterwards.

A typical traffic accident of the period occurred in Flitwick that Saturday. John Richardson was driving a brewery dray near the station when his horse was scared by the shriek of a Midland Railway express. It bolted, and Richardson fell off the cart and was injured by the horse's hooves.

Saturday was the meeting day for the members of the Bedford Rural Sanitary Authority, which looked after health matters outside of Bedford itself. They were worried by an outbreak of diptheria at Bolnhurst, which had begun on 3rd October. The problem was blamed on a London girl, who had had diptheria and came to Bolnhurst to convalesce. The 3rd October case had been a child who had played with the girl and by 17th October five people in the neighbouring house had also got the disease. By 1st November two children had died and then, just when it seemed the worst was over, the Authority learnt that another new case had been reported the previous Monday. The

Authority was worried that each case cost 30 shillings a week to handle at the Bedford Fever Hospital.

The Rural Sanitary Authority's meeting also discussed the problem of filthy pigsties at Great Barford and a disgraceful house in Bolnhurst (quite a shocking place, it seems!). The house had no water supply apart from what was collected from a ditch and an Inspector called to find the children 'half-dressed and lying on rags'. The husband earned 25 shillings a week, but his wife – though educated – was 'useless', so the children rarely went to school as they had too few clothes and were infested with vermin. The case was referred to the NSPCC.

Bedford's problems were handled by the Urban Sanitary Authority. Their main concern was that the poor people of the town were being blackmailed by the contractor responsible for collecting refuse. If they did not pay up, he would not take their rubbish away. The Authority felt that it would be better if refuse collection was handled by municipal employees than some dubious private contractor.

Another meeting that day was of the Bedford Poor Law Guardians. The principal case they discussed was of a Mr Arnold, who had been a teacher at Bedford Grammar School but was now being kept in a lunatic asylum at the Guardians' expense. Their attempts to get his father to pay something had met with failure so far.

During the day the police court sat to look at some minor local offences. One of these involved William George, a young man from Clapham. The previous Saturday he had enjoyed a good night's drinking with a friend and, when staggering home past a field, had said 'We will go and find our Sunday lunch'. George had killed a sheep, but was too drunk to hide the traces of his crime. His case was sent forward to the Quarter Sessions.

Saturday afternoon was the traditional time for football, as it still is. Some matches were of purely local interest, such as the tussle at Aspley Guise between Powage Press FC and Wolverton Town, the former winning 2-1. Clapham Rovers struggled through a 0-0 draw with Bedford Town, but Bedford

Swifts thrashed Arlesey 5-0. There was also a Bedford team called Queens Park Rangers.

However the 'top' match was at Luton, which was the best team in Bedfordshire, against Watford Rovers before a crowd of over 2,000. With Watford leading 4-3, the last few minutes of the match were played out in semi-darkness, during the course of which the referee disallowed a goal by Luton, to the disgust of local fans who for once had a genuine reason for the ref's apparent 'blindness'.

A different sporting fixture of local interest, but taking place outside the county, was a boxing match between Samuel 'Nutty' Nutt of Bedford and William 'Chicken' Lawson of Luton. This was held in High Holborn with stakes of £10 a side. 'Nutty' won in eight minutes.

During Saturday evening a bag of meat was stolen off the counter at a butcher's shop in Aspley Guise. The local constable followed the thief to Ridgmont, where he was able to arrest a man named Spring – who spent Saturday night in the lock-up at Woburn.

Sunday 29th was Nonconformist Temperance Sunday and fiery temperance sermons were preached throughout the county – except in the Anglican churches, of course. At Aspley Guise Mount Pleasant chapel they had two special sermons on the subject.

On the Monday the Bedford police court was open for business, dealing with the weekend's problem drinkers. John White, for example, was brought in accused of being drunk, disorderly and using bad language in Midland Road. He had been staying at the Royal Oak, but assaulted the housekeeper there, broke two panes of glass and was then arrested when he went out into the street. He continued to be a problem at the police station, where he broke seven panes of glass. White claimed that he suffered from sunstroke after a spell in India, but he was given 14 days hard labour to reflect on his problems.

The same morning an inquest was held at Bedford Workhouse on the body of Rose Gammons, a six month old baby. Rose's mother, who was unmarried, was said to come from 'a family which was the lowest of the low' in Thurleigh, and was 'an imbecile'. The verdict was of death by natural causes.

Monday also saw some property sales. A row of ten cottages at Kempston, which were rented out, were sold for £440. More exciting for many was the arrival in Bedford of Charles Keith's Circus for a week's residency. Top of the bill were Mademoiselle Alvira the juggler, Rosina Carlo on the hire wire, and miss Anna with her performing poodles. Most amazing of all, though, was Holturn the Cannon King – said to be capable of catching a cannonball, fired from a cannon, in his mouth.

During Monday afternoon and evening a series of snooker exhibition matches were held at the Bedford Conservative Club. These featured W.J. Peall, the reigning world champion, and G. Standon, a prominent professional from Luton. There was a dense crowd in the billiards room throughout the matches.

Wednesday 1st December was the day when the various local School Boards met. The Kempston School Board was pleased to hear that attendance was averaging 90%. An Inspector had complained to them that the school at Up End had too little heating, and the Board resolved to complain to the Rural Sanitary Authority that some children had to wade through two miles of muddy lane to get to school.

On the Wednesday evening the main social event was the dinner of the Bedford Volunteers at the Swan Hotel. Prizes were distributed to the members of the 'other ranks' who had been the best attenders at drills and exercises. The volunteers were rather like the modern Territorial Army.

In many ways, it seems, things have changed very little. At the end of the 19th century people got arrested for being drunk, went to watch football in Luton, and became involved in passionate arguments over seemingly minor local issues, just as they do today.

The Pilgrim's Progress

WITHOUT any doubt, the most famous writer to have been born in Bedfordshire was the 17th century religious author, John Bunyan. His name has become closely linked with the town of Bedford itself, though not always accurately – the story of his imprisonment in the gaol on Bedford bridge is merely a legend, for example. Bunyan has a prominent statue in Bedford, but his most enduring memorial will always be his most famous book – the *Pilgrim's Progress*.

Bunyan did not come from an illustrious family, a fact he made great play of in later life. He was born at Elstow in November 1628 to a family who had once, in generations gone by, been smallholders. Bunyan's great-great-grandfather was a 'common brewer' but it was his grandfather who had first shown signs of being a rebel against official Church policies – in 1617 he had been in trouble for calling the churchwardens liars.

The family in which Bunyan grew up earned their living from various types of minor trade, so that Bunyan himself claimed to be a tinker. We have only his own colourful account to tell us about his childhood, in which religion was influential though not dominant. At the age of about ten, John Bunyan was troubled with nightmares about Hell though this seems to have had little effect on him, for later in his youth he became notorious for 'cursing, swearing, lying and blaspheming'.

His family were successful enough to give him a chance of some schooling, but in November 1644 Bunyan joined the Parliamentary Army in its struggles against the Royalists. Bunyan enjoyed the life of a soldier and military images surface in his later writings, but there was little real fighting left to be involved with. He was posted to Newport Pagnell with a number of other Bedfordshire men and took part in the frequent religious discussions that were typical of the time. It was a period of many different opinions, some conservative and some highly radical; Bunyan had time to find out about Quakers, Ranters, Levellers and Diggers, the last of whom had a colony at Dunstable. The Newport Pagnell connection proved useful, though, for it was a bookseller from there who brought out Bunyan's first three works.

In 1647 he returned to Elstow and later got married. His daughter, Mary, who was blind, was born in 1650. There have been many suggestions that Bunyan's moral state at this time was not healthy – he seems to have married rather hastily, was not on good terms with his father, and referred to himself later as 'a great sin-breeder'. The young couple started their married life with hardly a possession between them; his wife brought two religious books, but they had not so much 'household stuff as a dish or a spoon betwixt us both'. His first wife died in 1658 and he married a girl called Elizabeth in 1659.

Soon after Mary was born, Bunyan seems to have started taking his religious beliefs more seriously. In 1653 he was accepted as a member of a nonconformist Bedford congregation and in 1655 was baptised as a full member of it. Soon after this he began preaching in the villages and hamlets around Bedford, no doubt using some of the connections he built up through his trade. He later wrote that he preached 'in the darkest places in the county', but was always conscious of his own failings: 'I went myself in chains to preach to them in chains', he wrote. In May 1656 he preached for the first time in Bedford itself.

At about the same time he began his writing with a series of pamphlets. Some, like *A Few Sighs From Hell,* attacked the

Quakers, while others chose the Church of England clergy as a target. They did not make him a popular man with the authorities.

Bunyan's style of preaching no doubt owed something to what he had learnt while listening to the arguments at Newport Pagnell, and he was soon identified as a trouble-maker. In February 1658 he was warned about his preaching and in November 1660 arrested for holding unlawful meetings – though his real offence was to have preached unacceptable things at these meetings. The local gentry disliked the 'licentious and destructive principle' in his preaching and saw him as a 'rabble-rouser' who needed to be stopped before he stirred up too much anti-Church and anti-Government feeling.

He had accumulated a number of powerful enemies such as Sir Henry Chester, who called Bunyan 'a pestilential fellow', and John Kelyng, the Bedford MP. At his trial, Elizabeth Bunyan spoke out in her husband's defence, arguing that 'because he is a tinker and a poor man, therefore he is despised and cannot have justice'. This sounded like dangerous talk, and did not help Bunyan's case, for he was committed to prison since he refused to stop preaching.

Bunyan spent about twelve years in prison, though conditions there varied. He was actually allowed out for a while at one point, and went to London to preach, while at other times he had to share the prison with up to 50 Quakers who were also 'inside' because of their beliefs; Bunyan became less hostile towards them.

During his early years in prison he continued to write such works as *Grace Abounding* and *The Holy City*. However, in 1666 the premises of his publisher were raided and Bunyan published nothing else for several years – probably because censorship was becoming more restrictive. It may have been during these apparently fallow years that Bunyan was working on the book that was to make him famous throughout the world, the *Pilgrim's Progress*.

In January 1672, while still in prison, Bunyan was appointed pastor of the Bedford congregation. He regained his freedom in March, just at the time when Charles II introduced his Declaration of Indulgence which made life for dissenters much easier. The Bedford congregation had met only erratically during the troubled 1660s, but it now registered as 'Congregational' and bought a barn to meet in. Bunyan set about the pastoral care of the church members and some of his experiences found their way into the *Pilgrim's Progress.*

His problems with the authorities, though, were still not over. The law continued to require attendance at the local parish church, and in 1675 Bunyan was summonsed for failure to comply with this. At first he went into hiding, but eventually spent the period from December 1676 to June 1677 back in prison.

Pilgrim's Progress was published in 1678 when the climate of censorship had become more relaxed. Bunyan had hesitated over the work for he was not sure if it was moral to write fiction about spiritual matters. The book was a great success and inspired a number of fake sequels, so that in 1684 Bunyan had to produce and publish a 'Part Two' of his own. In it he sought to correct the rather harsh impression given of the Pilgrim's family.

He continued to write for the rest of his life. *The Life & Death of Mr Badman* was said to contain a fair quantity of the 'original' John Bunyan, for the villain of the book is notorious for his swearing and other wicked habits. *The Holy War,* partly inspired by political struggles in Bedford itself, drew on his enthusiasm for military topics.

During the 1670s and 1680s Bunyan became a famous man and a popular preacher. He toured many counties and preached frequently in London, always to a packed hall. Charles Doe wrote that, 'If there were but one day's notice given, there would be more people come together to hear him preach than the meeting-house could hold'.

After the death of Charles II, James II succeeded to the throne but the troubled times continued. With rebellion in the air, and religious matters again sensitive, Bunyan took the prudent step in December 1685 of conveying all his property to his wife in case of further trouble with the authorities. He died in August 1688, just before William of Orange landed in England to ensure a Protestant monarchy. He died in a manner which befits the way he had lived, for the chill that killed him was caught on a journey made to reconcile a father and a son.

Bedford Broadcasting

WHEN people talk about the BBC, they usually assume that the first 'B' stands for 'British' and could hardly imagine that it might once have been the *Bedford* Broadcasting Corporation. Yet for four years during the Second World War, much of the BBC was based in Bedford and thousands of broadcasts were made from the town. International stars visited the town and the famous Glenn Miller set off on his fateful last journey from a Bedfordshire airfield.

At the start of the Second World War, the BBC Music Department was relocated to Bristol in order to escape the feared bombing raids on London. Although the stay in Bristol was a great success, Hitler's planes began to raid that city too in October 1940. The BBC needed a town within easy reach of London and chose to look at places along the railway line from St Pancras. They required ten studios, 30 offices and beds for the 200 staff. Although several towns closer to London were unable to help, the Mayor of Bedford volunteered his town's facilities and managed to arrange nearly everything in the space of two days.

A number of public buildings around Bedford were suitable for use as studios, especially the Corn Exchange and the Great Hall of Bedford School. Two hotels in Bushmead Avenue were also pressed into use for the BBC, but Sir Adrian Boult was very embarrassed when he arrived there to see the last of their elderly residents being packed off to somewhere less salubrious. Boult himself lived at Clapham for the next four years.

The move to Bedford was made during July 1941, with most of the orchestra travelling to Bedford on a special train from Bristol. It followed a very circuitous route in order to avoid London, but was equipped with the luxury of a dining car – probably one of the last to run during the war years! Boult was more eccentric in his means of travel – he cycled the whole distance from Bristol to Bedford via Aylesbury.

Both the BBC Symphony Orchestra and the Theatre Orchestra moved to Bedford, and actually used seven studios. The Theatre Orchestra was based in St Paul's church, while the Corn Exchange became a popular concert venue because of its organ. Most popular of all, though, was the Great Hall at Bedford School, which was ideal for a full orchestra and was used nearly every day.

The BBC's control centre was set up in the large hall at the Bunyan Meeting, and John Bunyan himself would have appreciated the irony of the religious broadcasting studio – it was in a converted billiards saloon in Castle Lane! More popular music was also performed, much of it at the C-Partners Hall off Ford End Road. Stars such as Bing Crosby, Marlene Dietrich and Glenn Miller played there.

The Corn Exchange was often used by the Symphony Orchestra for rehearsals and was appreciated as it was close to Woolworths where many of the musicians liked to go for refreshments. On one occasion Adrian Boult and Laurence Olivier went there to buy some incidental music for a play that was being recorded.

The first BBC concert in Bedford took place on 17th September 1941, following which there were some famous performances. On 8th December 1941 the first public performance of Prokofiev's *Alexander Nevsky* was given, with Peggy Ashcroft featured. On 21st December a special Birthday Concert was performed in honour of Joseph Stalin, to which munitions workers and the staff of the Russian Embassy were invited. It must have been one of the few occasions when a murderous tyrant was publicly honoured in Bedford!

A Roosevelt Birthday Concert was given on 30th January 1942, with a programme of American music. In June 1942 John Barbarolli conducted the BBC Symphony Orchestra for the first time while in September 1943 a performance of *Pilgrim's Progress* was given in the School Great Hall, starring Laurence Olivier. This was a good way of thanking Bedford for its hospitality as, due to censorship, the fact that the BBC was broadcasting from Bedford was never publicly aired.

The Symphony Orchestra did not spend all its time in Bedford, but used it as a base to visit other towns in the district. During Autumn 1941 it toured Luton, Kettering and Cambridge, for example.

Conditions in Bedford were not always ideal. The Great Hall was often so cold in winter that it caused problems for the fingers of the strings players. One wintry night there was also a gale blowing during a live transmission, and suddenly a window blew in. The long curtains flapped wildly and part of the Hall was plunged into darkness. The hour was saved by the school's Sergeant-Major, who climbed onto the window ledge and held the curtains in place until the end of the transmission.

During the summer of 1944 Glenn Miller was a regular user of the airfield at Twin Woods Farm to the north-west of Bedford, and on some sunny afternoons his band practised in the open there. Miller got a flat in Waterloo Road and his band gave their first Bedford performance on 9th July 1944 from the Corn Exchange.

Glenn Miller decided that he wanted to make a Christmas broadcast from Paris, and was impatient to set this up rather than hanging around in humble Bedford. On 15th December 1944 he arrived at the airfield and clambered into a Norseman monoplane with a couple of companions. The weather and visibility were poor, but Miller was determined to make the trip though it would seem likely that he had no authorisation. His plane disappeared into the December night and that evening a recording of his band, with Miller making the announcements, was played on the radio. But Miller was never seen again, and it is believed that his plane probably crashed into the sea.

The BBC was anxious to return to London, but this was delayed by the Germans' use of V1 and V2 rockets. An attempt was made to perform the 1944 Proms at the Royal Albert Hall, but they had to be switched to Bedford because of the rocket threat. This brought Sir Henry Wood to the town in his last year at the Proms.

By the summer of 1945 the musicians were becoming increasingly angry about the continued stay in Bedford and were anxious to return to London. Many of them went to the capital for the 1945 Proms and made it known that they would not go back to Bedford afterwards! This worried the BBC authorities, who feared that many of their best musicians would be persuaded to join other orchestras, so it was agreed to allow the return to London from 24th September 1945.

Thus over 8,000 broadcasts and Bedford's musical glory came to an end. During the time the BBC was in the town enemy planes were sighted only twice, and on only one occasion were bombs actually dropped. Strangely enough, there was only one air-raid on Bristol during the same period!

A Jump with the Devil

ONE village that had an especially bad reputation in the distant past was that of Marston Moretaine, between Bedford and Woburn. In the days when many Bedfordshire people followed the strict code of behaviour of the Puritans, the people of this village were said to be carefree types who never bothered about the rights or wrongs of what they were doing.

The more puritanical of folk warned that this 'do as you please' lifestyle could only end in tears – and probably Hell. For one young man their predictions came true, and his sorry end was marked by a stone called the Devil's Jumps, that stood in a field near the road to Lidlington and Woburn. When these stricter folk passed by with their children, they would point out the stone. 'Take care', they would warn, 'for the Devil himself is waiting to snatch wicked men off to the depths of Hell!'

In those times the vicar of Marston Moretaine was a hard-working and tireless man, who spent all his hours preaching the Gospel to his wayward people and attempting to guide them in the ways they led their lives. Yet it was a strange parish for a man to work in – and the parish church was odder still. Instead of the church and its tower forming one complete building, the tower stood entirely separate from the church. Halfway up the south side of this tower was an old archway, put there for no apparent purpose whatsoever. When the vicar had first arrived in the village he had questioned an

elderly inhabitant about the strange way the church had been built.

The old man had scratched his head and tried to look intelligent, but he had never really thought about it before. Then the answer had stirred within his muddled mind. 'Well, Vicar, the answer's simple', he had begun, 'folks round here like to do things their own way. If people tell us that a church and a tower should be joined together – well, that's a good reason why our church and tower should be kept apart'.

The vicar was not pleased by this answer, for it seemed to him that the folk of Marston Moretaine were a wilful lot who did not like to listen to advice. He could see that the task of being their spiritual guide was going to be a difficult one.

The farmers of the district, despite this local characteristic, were generally a hard-working lot. From Monday to Saturday they toiled in the fields or looked after their animals, and on Sunday morning they went to church. The vicar could stand in his pulpit and look down upon row after row of them, sitting quietly with a hat on their knees and a pious expression on their faces. The problems, though, began after the church service was finished.

The common belief among more puritanical people was that the Sabbath should be set aside for godly activities – reading the Bible, going to church, and praying. The belief among the people of Marston Moretaine, though, was that once you had done your duty by going to church you could do whatever you liked. So after church many of them would drift off to the inn, or start running about in some lively game. A few, it was said, even enjoyed a spot of gambling.

Chief among these habitual breakers of the Sabbath peace was a young farmer who owned a field close to the church. He was a healthy and boisterous fellow, with friends of exactly the same nature. Every Sunday they would sit quietly in church but, as soon as the service was over, they would rush out shouting and laughing. Usually they went straight to the nearby field owned by the young man, where they would fool around like young puppies. This annoyed the vicar greatly, for the field was so close to the church that all the congregation could watch the disgraceful frolicking that the young men indulged in.

The vicar decided to try and put a stop to the games. One day he met the young man in a lane near the church, and used the opportunity to try out a few friendly words of warning. 'You really must try to set a better example about how to behave on Sundays', the vicar said.

'Why?' asked the young man, who did not see any reason for a vicar to direct how he spent his leisure time. 'I can have some fun if I feel like it, can't I?'

'You can have fun whenever you like, but not on the Sabbath', the vicar warned. 'If you carry on like this you could end up in Hell!'

The young farmer did not believe this, and saw no reason why he should abandon his favourite game of 'Jumps' just because of a clergyman's idle threat. Adopting an arrogant tone, for he was very pleased with himself, he became sarcastic with the vicar. 'What, do you think the Devil himself is going to join in?'

The vicar stamped his foot in rage and frustration, for there seemed no way to make the young man realise that his soul was in mortal danger. The farmer would not listen, but the Devil himself did – for he had taken up residence on top of the church tower from where he could observe all the wicked activities of the local people.

The only course of action open to the vicar was to prepare a sermon on the subject of Sabbath-breaking. For the rest of the week he laboured in his study, making sure that his message was as clear as the tower of his church.

The following Sunday he looked down from his pulpit on the faces of the usual congregation. The young farmer was there as normal, sitting two rows from the front; he wore a self-satisfied expression, as if to assure the vicar that he had not yet been snatched away by the Devil.

'The Lord commanded us to keep the Sabbath holy', the vicar began, 'but in this village its sanctity is much abused.

I have evidence that drinking, gambling and even public sports take place in Marston Moretaine on Sundays'.

All this had no impact on the young farmer or his friends, who took the view that the vicar said these sorts of things because it was part of his job, just as tilling the ground was part of theirs.

At the end of the service the young farmer and his friends put on their hats, walked out into the sunshine, and then ran through the churchyard into the field. 'What shall we play?' one of them called out. 'Jumps!' the others shouted. Jumps was a noisy and energetic game, involving jumping onto each other's shoulders – a game specially unsuitable for a Sunday. Unknown to the young men, it was also a game that the Devil himself loved to play – especially if he could find anyone else who liked to play on the Sabbath.

As the young men ran laughing around the field, the vicar heard their shrieks and his heart was filled with despair. But up on the church tower the Devil had perched himself in the old doorless arch on the south face, from where he had an excellent view of the young men.

The Devil watched until the young farmer who owned the field was running around without anyone on his back. This was the Devil's chance, and he took a giant leap from off the church tower and landed . . . on the young farmer's shoulders!

The young farmer felt the sudden impact and realised that this was someone heavier than his usual friends; but then he felt the Devil's hot breath on his neck and smelt the sulphurous breath of Satan himself. For a second or two he struggled to free himself from the Devil's iron grip, but Satan wrapped his taloned legs around the young man and took one more leap.

They leapt up into the air and then, to the horror of everyone, a chasm suddenly opened up in the field. Down into it plunged the Devil and the young farmer, headlong into Hell. The other gamesters felt the heat from the fires of Hell, then the chasm closed up again. The field returned almost to normal, except for a single stone left standing where the farmer had disappeared. From then on it was known as the Devil's Jumps.

As can be imagined, the next Sunday saw a much larger congregation than usual in the church, and no-one at all ventured to the inn, where the gaming tables were quiet. As for the young man, he was never seen again, for the vicar's warning about the dangerous state of his soul had proved to be true.

Royalty and Romance

AMPTHILL is an attractive little town, which once had a powerful castle where Henry VIII's first wife, Catherine of Aragon, was held as a virtual prisoner for a while. Perhaps it was this combination of powerful stone walls and a pious lady badly treated, that led Victorian hearts to think of romance and chivalry. Whatever the reason, Ampthill took centre stage in a romantic Victorian blockbuster named *Ampthill Towers.*

The story begins in 1532, a year when King Henry VIII was still in his prime and when the religious troubles had not yet stricken the county. That year a young gypsy was seen in the neighbourhood and, since there was a common prejudice against such people, he was arrested as a vagrant and a likely thief. The Ampthill beadle was told to punish the gypsy in the usual way – by tying him to the back of a cart and dealing out a public flogging. The beadle was all ready to start work when elderly Sir Hugh Conquest rode up from Houghton, for it was Sir Hugh who had ordered the punishment.

Sir Hugh was about to instruct the beadle to begin when his attention was caught by the sight of a stranger on horseback appearing at the other end of the street. The young man introduced himself as Sir Guy Beaumont, from Mixbury in Oxfordshire. 'I am the nephew of Sir John Gostwick of

Willington, and at his home I will be staying tonight. But first I wish to visit the fair Cainhoe Castle, home of the lordly St Amand family'.

Sir Hugh decided to let the gypsy off his punishment and invited Sir Guy back with him for lunch. On the way they rode steadily, but Honed the gypsy, grateful for his deliverance, kept up a ready pace behind them. Sir Guy chatted merrily to the older man, explaining how he was but a poor knight although he had recently had a temporary post at the Court, in attendance on Queen Catherine.

At Houghton, Sir Hugh's wife proved a more attentive audience than her husband, and rapidly deduced that Guy was in love with Beatrice St Amand. Honed, though, did not prove as popular with Sir Hugh's head huntsman, Giles Hodgkin, who could see no use for a gypsy.

'Good', said Sir Guy, 'for I have left my servant back at Dunstable, where he is stricken with illness'. In no time at all it was arranged that Honed should accompany Sir Guy.

Soon Guy was back on his horse and riding thoughtfully towards Cainhoe, unsure what to do. Despite his love, he had hardly ever spoken to Beatrice and knew nothing of her father. Besides, he was only a poor knight and he knew of at least one rival – Maurice de Bretigny, a favourite of King Henry VIII.

As Cainhoe Castle came into sight he reined in his horse and waited by some trees, looking across to it. Honed stood patiently beside him, catching his breath. Sir Guy heard youthful voices and saw that some horses were being exercised in a field near the castle. But suddenly there was a shout, and one of the horses bolted out of control with its inexperienced rider helpless. With a leap in his heart, Sir Guy realised that the girl on the horse was none other than the beautiful Beatrice, whose very life seemed to be in danger.

Guy spurred his own horse forward and out of the trees. It was clear to him that Beatrice lacked the strength to bring the horse back under control and so he raced up to it, looping his own arm through its reins. With a shuddering heave he caught the reins firm, but the power of the horse nearly broke his arm before it steadied and stood panting. Beatrice slid off the horse with the sudden jolt, but was unhurt though clearly terrified.

Of course St Amand soon heard of the rescue of his youngest daughter, and invited the knight to his castle. Sir Guy stayed for supper and listened to the conversation, which was all about the troubles of Queen Catherine. St Amand was angry that Henry VIII sought to throw her off in order to marry Anne Boleyn, and Beatrice declared her own undying allegiance to the patient Catherine. Sir Guy sided with them in the discussion, though he knew the King conferred no favours on those who took against him on the issue.

It was late in the evening by the time Sir Guy left, reluctantly, for Willington. Sir John was pleased to see him, but had other things on his mind. Henry VIII had declared that he was to visit Ampthill Castle the next week, and it was Sir John's duty to attend on him there. The old nobleman was scandalised by the news that Henry was to bring Anne with him, treating her as Queen even though he was still married to Catherine of Aragon.

Sir Guy offered to accompany Sir John to Ampthill, motivated largely by a belief that he might see Beatrice there. Late in the evening he decided to take a closer look at the events at the castle. Knowing the area well, he slipped into the grounds and watched Maurice de Bretigny officiously ordering people around. It became clear that Maurice had been entrusted with a senior role in the guarding of the King.

After a while Maurice spotted Guy in the trees. Perhaps he had had some word that Guy was a rival in love for Beatrice, for he sneered at him. 'What are you doing here? You have no right to be near the King. Guards!' Maurice shouted the last word, but the guards were a few hundred yards away.

Sir Guy did not intend to be arrested in such a ridiculous fashion. As Maurice grabbed at him he pushed out, and de Bretigny fell to the floor. Guy turned away, unaware that Maurice was drawing a dagger behind his back. Yet just as the blade was poised to strike between the shoulder blades, a dark shape dropped silently from a nearby tree. Maurice's hand was struck as if by a spirit, and the dagger went sailing through the air before the shape disappeared as silently as it had arrived.

Guy was startled by the sudden commotion, saw the glint of the dagger in the air, and drew his sword. He turned to see the startled Maurice standing defenceless, but then the guards were upon them and there was no escape. Guy spent the night in a cell high up in the roof of the castle.

The next day had been set aside by the King for hunting. The hunt was attended by all the local gentry and organised by Sir Hugh. St Amand and Beatrice also came, but knew they were out of place at the King's hunt, and soon turned their horses back towards Cainhoe. As they were leaving, Honed appeared beside them. He told them of what had happened to Sir Guy and how, even at that moment, he was languishing in the cell at Ampthill Castle.

The next day Maurice de Bretigny talked to the King about the 'traitors' who opposed his marriage to Anne Boleyn. Now Henry was no fool, and he recognised de Bretigny for the unctuous bootlicker that he was – but such people could be useful. Maurice hinted that Sir Guy was one such traitor and the King decided he would have to be dealt with.

That night at the castle there was a banquet. Servants streamed in and out of every building in a variety of costumes, so no-one paid any attention to Honed when he walked in calmly carrying an empty dish. Honed made his way up onto the roof of the castle, then let himself down by rope to the window of Guy's cell. The two were soon able to weaken the bars on the window, retie the rope, and rapidly made their escape into the darkness of the park.

For a long time nothing was heard of Sir Guy, but at last he could keep away from Beatrice no longer. With the pressure for his capture having died down, Guy was able to meet St Amand, Sir Hugh and Sir John in reasonable safety. They discussed how to get Guy out of his problems, and at this point it occurred to them that the answer lay in proving Maurice had drawn a dagger on Guy. There had, of course, been a third person present that night – the 'unearthly spirit' that had dropped from the trees, better known to his friends as Honed.

It was arranged that they should all go to London, with Sir Guy as the 'prisoner' of Sir John. They travelled down at the time of the Coronation, for Henry had secured his divorce and was to marry Anne and make her Queen. They stood in the dense crowd and watched as a procession of dignitaries paraded by. Among the procession was the oily Maurice de Bretigny, and he was shocked to suddenly catch a glimpse of the hated Sir Guy.

Maurice shouted for the guards, but there was nothing he could do. Sir John explained that Sir Guy was his prisoner and was being brought to London to see the King – what business was it of Maurice? As Maurice turned away, a voice called out 'A stab in the back disgraces not him who receives it, but him who gives it'. Maurice turned back, but he did not recognise the grinning face of Honed.

Sir John arranged an audience before Henry VIII, and the King naturally asked for Maurice to be present too. At first the Bedfordshire party kept quiet about the existence of Honed, but argued that the attempted stabbing had been witnessed. Maurice, who was not good under pressure, tried to bluff his way out of it and was tricked in his answers – he revealed that there had been 'no-one there but a spirit'. Then the spirit was produced!

Henry, who found Maurice useful but had no great love for him, laughed. He found it quite believable that Maurice should have tried such a thing, and highly amusing that he had been proved a liar by a mere gypsy. He declared Sir Guy a free man.

Of course it goes without saying that Sir Guy went back to Bedfordshire and married Beatrice. They may not have been the richest couple in the county, but they were certainly the happiest.

The Mystery of the Lost Balloon

ON the evening of 16th March 1891 two men were walking near Kempston Hardwick when their attention was caught by an unusual sight – a large hot-air balloon was skimming across the treetops in an erratic fashion. The men quickly realised that the balloon was too low to be travelling safely and could see no sign of any passengers in the basket that hung beneath it.

A rope trailed from the basket and the men decided to try and chase the balloon and to 'capture' it – who knows, there could be a reward for finding a lost hot-air balloon! So they ran across fields for about a mile and saw the balloon become entangled in a hedge at Mr Dimmock's farm, near Wootton. They were able to catch up with it and secure it by tying the rope to a tree.

The two men now had a problem. What did they do with the balloon? At first they stood around, thinking that someone who owned it might have followed at ground-level and would soon catch up. But no-one arrived, and it was now quite dark. The balloon was only partially inflated and, at about 9 pm, it suddenly collapsed in on itself like a great creature dying.

The men waited until after 11 pm, but still no-one had arrived to claim the balloon. After a brief discussion, they decided that the best thing would be to let the police look after it, for it was getting cold in Dimmock's field by this time and at least the police were paid to stand around doing nothing.

In due course Superintendent Quenby arrived to take charge of the matter. His first theory was that someone had fallen out of the balloon 'car', but there had been no reports of any such thing at Bedford police station. When he looked into the car or basket, he found only two clues – a black bag, containing a thermometer and, suspiciously, a large dagger! Quenby's mind must have immediately considered the possibility of murder: imagine it – the first 'balloon murder' and he would gain the fame for solving it!

Quenby therefore 'arrested' the balloon and, when daylight arrived, arranged for it to be taken into custody at Bedford police station. After that, though, enquiries drew a blank and a report of the lost balloon appeared in the local paper. No dead body had been found, no-one had reported having a hot-air balloon stolen, and the only information the newspaper could reveal was that the balloon bore the word 'Adventure' painted on its side.

The police received an urgent telegram, signed by Thomas Bartram of Brixton. It said that the balloon belonged to Mr Bartram but that he could not collect it since he was leaving for Gibraltar that evening – would the police mind posting it back to him? It seems very likely that this telegram was a hoax.

However, the next contact made with the police was much more plausible. A letter arrived from Arthur Williams and William Smith of Battersea, claiming that the balloon was theirs and enclosing a press cutting describing their hazardous first attempt to fly it.

The two men had decided to make a trial trip in their balloon from Battersea, and it had been inflated with the help of Mr Pilbrow of the Gas Light Company together with 30,000 ft of gas. At about 4.30 pm on 16th March, Smith and Williams had climbed aboard and taken the balloon up to a height of 5,000 ft above Battersea.

At this point things started to go badly wrong. Once over Chelsea, the balloon lurched into a sudden dive. The two aeronauts threw out three bags of sand ballast and by this method just managed to clear the rooftops along the King's Road. However the sudden jettisoning of ballast took them up to a greater height than they had expected – about three miles above the streets of London!

The men consulted their thermometer and it confirmed their feelings – the temperature at this altitude was 15 degrees below freezing. The balloon began to drift north-west and gradually lost height; over Neasden it suddenly began to drop more rapidly, catching the men unprepared so that it hit the ground before they could throw out more ballast.

The car hit the ground so sharply that Williams was thrown out altogether and landed in a ditch. Smith attempted to secure the balloon by throwing out the grapnel, but the sudden loss of Williams' weight proved disastrous – the balloon shot skywards once more and the grapnel rope broke under the strain. It was this rope that was eventually used to secure the balloon.

Poor Smith was carried up to a height of over three and a half miles, so that he wondered if he was about to freeze to death. However, at this height the atmosphere was very thin and the gas in the balloon began to expand, causing its valve to open with the pressure. Smith opened the valve more fully and the balloon began to descend, at first under his control, and then – suddenly and definitely – out of his control! It fell three and a half miles in the space of two minutes before slowing up as the atmosphere thickened again. Over Harrow the car came close to the ground and Smith jumped out of it – preferring to risk injury rather than likely death if he trusted himself to the balloon any longer.

As soon as Smith had jumped out, the balloon shot up into the sky again and disappeared from view heading in a northerly direction. This, Smith and Williams claimed, was the balloon that had been found at Wootton.

Having been the subject of one hoax, the police may have been suspicious about this extraordinary tale – but one detail clinched it. Smith and Williams said the balloon was called 'Adventurer', not 'Adventure', and a check by the police proved this to be the case. And what about the long dagger – had there been a murder? The explanation was simple – it had been used to slit open the bags of sand ballast before they were dropped from the balloon.

Highdays and Holidays

IN past centuries, when Bedfordshire was a rural county little affected by metropolitan habits, it had a number of colourful and distinctive social customs. Each marked a special occasion and provided a glint of colour and light in a year that, for most people, consisted of endless drudgery and toil.

Customs to do with May Day were particularly common and many of these survived into the 20th century. One village that was especially celebrated for its May Day festivities was Tilsworth. On May Day eve the young men of the village would make a tour of all the houses in the district where attractive young maidens could be found; at each house they would leave a stick in the ground or leaning against the side of the building. Whilst walking around, they recited an old song which neatly linked the three themes of May festivities – ancient fertility ritual, modern desire for money and a timeless thirst for alcohol!

> 'Today today is the first of May
> The Spring time of the year
> And if you please on another day
> We'll taste of your strong beer.

And if strong beer you have not got
We'll be content with small,
We'll pledge thee well against that day
And give God thanks for all.

A branch of may I have you brought
And at your door it stands,
It is but a sprout, but it's well budded out,
It is the work of our Lord's hands.

Arise arise you pretty fair maids
And view your may so gay,
Or else you'll say on another day
We brought you not your may.

I have a purse in my pocket
Tied with a silken string
We'll thank you for some silver
To line it well within.'

Similar traditions were popular in many Bedfordshire villages, though with slight variations. At Bromham the young men gathered branches from the thorn bush rather than offering sprigs of may. More waspishly, the men of Keysoe handed out various types of branch to the unmarried women of the district and these were graded according to the perceived qualities of the women and maidens: an unwanted spinster got a piece of a briar bush.

At Northill, near Sandy, a May Bush cart toured the village accompanied by about ten 'Moggies', whose name seems to have been an insulting reference to the people of nearby Moggerhanger. The Moggies carried tall beribboned staves and were attended by a shabbily dressed man and 'woman' with blackened faces.

Other villagers marked May Day with less exuberant celebrations. At Shelton the schoolchildren would walk around the houses with a garland and dolls, singing songs. Sometimes they put several dolls into a basket, perhaps as a symbol of new babies.

At Sutton, May Day was marked by a feast in which the main ingredient was frumenty – made from hulled wheat boiled in milk with sugar, raisins and plums. The same mixture was eaten on Shrove Tuesday and Easter Day.

Another great day in the rural calendar was Plough Monday. This was always the first Monday to fall after 6th January and signalled the real beginning of farm work for the new year. At Shelton any boys or men who did farm work would put on odd costumes and masks, before patrolling the village streets in search of money. They would go up to cottages and knock on the door, singing out the traditional song, 'Give a poor plough boy a halfpenny or a penny'. When allowed into a cottage, they would sing and dance in exchange for alcohol or money.

Another tradition linked with the farming calendar was at Blunham, where the completion of wheat-sowing was marked by the farmers' wives. They baked cakes of sweet dough and caraway seeds, called Siblett cakes, for distribution to their friends. Food also featured on Palm Sunday, which was often called Fig Sunday as fig cakes were eaten; the first Sunday in July was known as Gooseberry Pie day for similar reasons.

Shrove Tuesday was another date in the calendar that provided an excuse for some fun. At Pulloxhill the children played a game called 'Threading the tailor's long needle', an excuse for shouting and calling while taking part in a long procession.

Bells featured in several Bedfordshire customs. At Toddington on Shrove Tuesday the church bell was always rung at 11.50 am and this was known as the 'Pan Bell', for its purpose was to warn the housewives to start frying. Another Toddington tradition was for the children to gather on Conger Hill at noon that day, for they were told that if they put an ear to the ground they would be able to hear an old lady frying her pancakes deep within the hillside.

Clearly bells were important in Toddington, for there was another custom that was practised by the children of the village whenever they heard the sound of Chalgrove's bells. Chiming in with the bells, they would sing out, 'Hang Frank Hall, his wife and all'. This custom was common in the 1840s and was said to be linked with the Hall family who had lived in the district in the 1750s.

For the people of Bedford, the feast day of St Simon and St Jude on 28th October was especially important. The day was marked by the cooking of a special dish made from warden pears, cinnamon and cloves cooked in red wine.

The eve of St Mark's day was especially important to young Bedfordshire ladies. In northern parts of the county the women and girls met in silence that evening to make a 'dumb cake' and at midnight each ate a slice without uttering a word before going quietly up the stairs to bed. It was said that the girl would be chased upstairs by the shadow of her future sweetheart, but great importance was placed upon the girl getting into bed before the shadow could catch her. What happened if the shadow caught her? Sadly, we do not know!

Oak Apple Day was celebrated in a number of places throughout Bedfordshire. At Dunstable and Caddington the churches were dressed with oak branches in what must have been a bizarre mixture of pagan belief and Christian architecture. At Toddington, villagers placed boughs of oak in their doorways. In eastern parts of the county children were expected to go to school with an oak-leaf buttonhole; if they failed to do this, they would be stopped and 'whipped' by boys armed with stinging nettles.

Some odd customs even existed in some of the county's parish churches. At Tilsworth the men all took Holy Communion first, followed by the women; however, at Stanbridge the reverse pattern applied. In Tilsworth church it was also the custom for the men and women to sit separately.

Of course the greatest day of all was Christmas. Nowadays the whole of Britain does more or less the same thing on Christmas Day, but up until the 1800s each district had its own traditions. At Potton the normal practice was to bake enormous Apple Florentines on massive pewter dishes. This was baked just like a pie, but a quart of hot spiced ale was always added.

Perhaps the strangest custom of all was held each year at Biddenham on 22nd September – St Agatha's Day. A white rabbit was decorated with scarlet ribbons and taken around the village. Any unmarried woman who met the procession had to point two fingers of the left hand at the rabbit and say:

'Gustin, Gustin, lacks a bier
Maidens, maidens, bury him here.'

This custom was said to date back to the Crusades, but what it all meant is lost in the mists of time!

The Luton 'Peace' Riot

PERHAPS it is typical of human nature that celebrations organised to commemorate the return of peace after years of bloodshed could arouse such bad feelings that days of riot and destruction were the result. Sadly this is what happened in Luton in 1919, for the riots that broke out there were so serious that the Town Hall was destroyed and the Mayor fled the town in a state of nervous terror.

Though the First World War actually ended on the 11th November 1918, the terms of the peace settlement were not decided upon until the following year. News of the signing of the Versailles Treaty reached Luton on the evening of 28th June 1919. Here, at last, was the official end of the worst war known to man – a war which had caused much suffering to many people from the Luton area. Full of self-importance in his official role at such a crucial time, the Mayor of Luton, Alderman Henry Impey, made an official announcement of the news from the steps of the Town Hall.

By the time Impey made his speech, the news had already travelled around the town. A large crowd gathered around the Town Hall, shouting and singing in celebration. Some brought fireworks with them, while others had visited the town's many hostelries – a combination that was not conducive to public

PEACE
EX-SERV
'GIVE US WO

safety. Soon enough high spirits got the better of commonsense, and a number of fireworks were thrown about among the crowd. Several people were injured and this cast a shadow over the evening.

Throughout Britain towns and cities began to plan how they would mark the official end of the war. In Luton the Council took the lead, but there were worries that the boisterous and dangerous scenes of 28th June could be repeated. Impey's Council therefore drew up some limited plans, restricted by a tight budget, and without consulting the two different groups for demobilised ex-servicemen that had already been formed in the district. The Council proposed some special events to be held on 19th July. Sufficient money was available for a procession, five bands, decorated floats, the floodlighting of the Town Hall, and a banquet for the members of the Corporation and their guests – to be held in the Town Hall assembly rooms.

These plans stirred up considerable anger in the district. They seemed to exclude all those who had made the greatest sacrifices – the widows, the disabled and the orphans. It was pointed out that all those who would be attending the victory banquet would be people who had spent a comfortable war in Luton. Feelings about 'them' and 'us' began to stir in Luton, especially when it became known that celebration plans in nearby Dunstable were much more generous to the disadvantaged.

The result of all this was that a rival celebrations committee was set up on 4th July. This group reflected the wishes of the ex-servicemen, most of whom were drawn from Luton's working classes, and planned two days of festivities. Their intention was for the events to culminate in a mass rally of servicemen, a parade through the town, and then a thanksgiving service to be held at Wardown Park. The idea was enthusiastically supported by most of Luton's clergymen.

The new committee was stunned when it learned that the Corporation had refused permission for it to use Wardown Park. Tempers began to rise, fuelling widespread discontent among the ex-servicemen. A number had returned home to find that their old jobs had been taken or, worse still, that ex-prisoners of war were being employed in their place. Unemployment was making many turn to politics and the example of Russia and the Bolshevik Revolution was discussed. Three men were arrested in Luton for burning the Union Jack.

Perhaps worried at the course events were taking, the Corporation offered the use of Pope's Meadow instead of the Park. Finally Lady Wernher informed the Corporation that the rival committee could use the park at Luton Hoo for their celebration; the Corporation delayed in passing on this information and so incurred further wrath.

As the day for the official celebrations, 19th July, approached, tension in Luton rose. Alderman Impey learned of rumours that a concerted attempt was to be made to break up the Corporation's peace banquet. He therefore arranged for extra police to be brought to the town from St Albans, Bedford and Cambridgeshire.

On 19th July the official procession was formed up with a few war veterans at the front, with the intention of marching through Luton to the Town Hall. At this moment it was discovered that one of the ex-servicemen's organisations, the Comrades of the Great War, had prepared a float to join the procession. The float was on the theme of Jack Cornwell VC, but came as a great surprise to the other group, the Discharged Sailors' and Soldiers' Association. A certain amount of rivalry already existed between these two groups. The 'Comrades' tended to be more conservative in their attitudes, while the 'Discharged' had been set up by two Liberal MPs and had more left-wing views. The latter were therefore highly offended at what they saw as a betrayal by the 'Comrades'. Their own intention had been to picket the parade by waving banners – the disabled were to have one that read 'Don't pity us. Give us work'.

Nonetheless the parade took place and eventually reached the Town Hall. The Mayor and a number of other dignitaries came out to the front of the building to address the crowds, and then the trouble began. There is conflicting evidence as to exactly what incited the crowd to violence; one account says that one of the Mayor's companions was overheard in making an insulting comment about the ex-servicemen, while another story says that the Mayor himself incurred the wrath of the 'Discharged' by publicly thanking the 'Comrades' for their support.

Whatever the actual cause, it would seem that a few careless words ignited the discontent that had been building up in the town since the end of the war. The crowd began to jeer the Mayor's speech, so that he and his companions retreated inside the building. A number of police guarded the doors, but they were no match for the angry crowd. One furious man stood on the Town Hall steps and cried out, 'I'll give the Mayor five minutes to come out. If he does not come out, then we'll fetch him!'

The crowd forced its way past the police and into the Town Hall with the deliberate intention of stopping the banquet. The Mayor fled to the police station, but the crowd ransacked much of the building. At the Town Hall was a clock that had been bought to commemorate the end of another war – the Crimean – and this was destroyed in the rioting. Then the crowd set off for his house, hoping to find him there – but Impey wisely remained in the safe custody of the police.

From this point the situation in Luton deteriorated rapidly. The forces of law and order were plainly unable to control a mob intent on expressing its anger and frustration, but many others also joined in to steal what they could amongst the chaos. As evening wore on, many appeared on the streets dead drunk.

At 11 pm the Corporation had planned to light flares around the town, but the crowd had other ideas. They returned to the Town Hall, forced their way back in, and set it on fire. After the rioting the Corporation mace was recovered 'in a blackened condition'.

The Fire Brigade was sent to the scene, several of whose men were ex-servicemen themselves. However the crowd had no mercy and attacked them with stones and bottles. Some of the mob even tried to link one of the fire hoses up to a petrol pump so as to help the Town Hall burn more fiercely. Fourteen firemen were injured, of whom four were detained in hospital.

Shops around the Town Hall were looted by the crowd. A piano was 'liberated' from a music shop and dragged into the street, where it was used for a 'wild dance' in which a number of women joined. When order was finally regained, 25 people were arrested for looting.

The events of 19th July and the early hours of the 20th were only calmed down when a detachment of troops arrived from the camp at Biscot Mill. This could have been a dangerous moment for the authorities, for many of the soldiers were only awaiting demobilisation themselves and could easily have sided with the crowd. In fact they did not, and nor did the crowd attack them; for the time being, calm returned to the streets of Luton.

Although Sir Leonard Dunning was sent by the Home Office to investigate this major collapse of law and order, the problems did not stop immediately. There was continued trouble over at least the next two days and nights, with crowds gathering and stones being thrown.

After the disturbances followed the recriminations. The spectre that haunted many minds was that the trouble in Luton was connected with the feared growth of Communism among the disenchanted ex-soldiers. It was easier for the Council, of course, if outside factors could be blamed rather than the Mayor's insensitive approach to the whole celebrations issue. The presence of 'inflammatory agents' from outside the town was discussed. There were also reports that a man had been seen to wave the Red Flag from a window of the Town Hall at the height of the riot, with a female accomplice beside him. Could Luton be the first stage in a Communist-inspired wave of rebellion?

The Corporation blamed the disturbances on the inadequate allowances being paid to the men who returned from the war. Having braved the horrors of the trenches, they had expected to return to a decent standard of living but unemployment was high in Luton. The Town Clerk, however, blamed the riots on 'Bolshevism, anarchy, drunkenness and criminality'. Not a word about the crude, insensitive and elitist behaviour of the Corporation!

For a week or two after the riot arrests were made on a daily basis, the majority being for looting or vandalism. Emily Tilcock, aged 49, was charged with stealing three odd slippers from a looted shop. Fred Plater was found to have dressed up as a clergyman to take part in the riot, and took the opportunity to steal two boots; when the police visited his home they found the illicit clerical garb. Plater could at least plead that he was an ex-soldier with a grievance but this could not be said of Maud Kitchener, who wore soldier's clothes during the riot – and in fact there were several reports of soldiers in uniform taking part. An ex-schoolmaster was arrested for throwing missiles at the Fire Brigade; he pleaded that his wife had died while he was in the army and he was now suffering from shell-shock. Most of those arrested were dealt with fairly lightly, perhaps for fear of creating 'martyrs'.

Perhaps the saddest figure of all in the aftermath of the Luton Peace Riot was the Mayor, Alderman Impey. After the worst of the riot he was advised to leave the town for his own safety, and initially retreated to Norfolk with his wife, whose health was broken by the tumultuous events of July 1919. Impey seems to have made only two brief visits to Luton after that, and retired to the isolated Lincolnshire coast town of Sutton-on-Sea. There, it was said, he never went out of doors after dusk and always kept the doors and windows of the house bolted – in his declining years the vision of the Luton riot continued to haunt him, though in death he was brought back to the town for burial.

Now Luton has another Town Hall which, in an ironic way, is the town's real commemoration of the end of the First World War.

The Miracle of Westoning

IT was in the autumn, probably about the year 1210, that a poor man called Fulke agreed to do some ploughing for a man named Ailward from the same district. The crops had been gathered in, and now Ailward needed a labourer to turn over the soil so that the winter cold could break up the heavy earth ready for next year's crop. Fulke agreed to perform the onerous task, a price of twopence being agreed upon – to be paid when the job had been finished.

Fulke got on with his task straight away, quickly ploughing the half acre and expecting to be paid his twopence. But Ailward, who was a bad-tempered, mean-spirited man, did not pay, and whenever Fulke met him made one excuse or another as to why he did not happen to have the money just at that moment.

December 21st was St Thomas of Canterbury's Day, and in Westoning this was always the excuse for three days of feasting, drinking and revelry. On one of the days of the festival, the despondent Fulke found his way into the cottage of the beerseller, where he came face to face with Ailward.

Ailward, who was never really short of a penny or two, was quite drunk, since he had spent the best part of the entire festival in the beerseller's cottage. Seeing this, Fulke went up to him and asked for the twopence he was owed.

'Ailward', he said, 'I worked hard and honestly on your land. Now the time has come for you to pay me what is owed'. 'Pay you?' laughed Ailward, grinning at his friends and slopping beer all over the table, 'Pay you for what? I don't remember you having done any work for me'.

Fulke reminded Ailward of exactly what he had done, but still Ailward denied it. Then Fulke decided on a clever plan which, he hoped, would get the other drinkers onto his side. 'Well, as I claim you owe me twopence, and you say you owe me nothing, I think we should meet halfway. You pay me one penny, and we'll use the other penny to buy everyone a drink to celebrate St Thomas.'

At this suggestion there were roars of approval, for though Ailward was surrounded by drinking companions who liked him, they liked free drink even more. 'Go on Ailward', they shouted, 'free drinks for everyone!' Ailward did not like this at all. He swung a fist at the irritating Fulke, then stormed out of the cottage in a drunken rage.

Staggering under the effect of the drink, he made as straight as he could for the poor hovel where Fulke lived with his family. Ailward kicked the door in with all the anger he could muster, and shocked the children by bursting in cursing and shouting. Pushing them aside, he proceeded to wreck the few things that poor Fulke owned. Having done this, he decided on another malicious plan – to ruin Fulke's livelihood. The wicked Ailward then tried to steal Fulke's hedging gloves and whetstone, but at this point the alcohol finally overcame him and he collapsed into a corner of the cottage, with the hedging equipment still in his hands.

Seizing their opportunity, the children fled from the cottage and ran straight to the beerseller's house. They called for their father, and Fulke came running. He burst into his cottage to find Ailward slightly revived, and clambering tipsily over the wrecked furniture. Fulke picked up the whetstone and struck his adversary a solid blow on the head, so that Ailward collapsed onto the floor unconscious once more.

Fulke went to get the beadle, and Ailward was arrested and thrown into prison at Bedford. Whilst in the dungeon there, Ailward vigorously proclaimed his innocence and called upon St Thomas of Canterbury to witness to this. Ailward had been baptised on the eve of Whitsun; there was a common belief that this led to people having the special protection of St Thomas, who had been declared a saint after his murder in 1170. The priests in Bedford were impressed by Ailward's faith in his supposed spiritual mentor, and gave him food – a regular supply of something to eat was by no means certain for a prisoner in those days.

It was arranged that Ailward should appear before the Assizes at Leighton Buzzard. There was obviously a lot of evidence against him on the charges to do with the wrecking of Fulke's cottage, but Ailward still maintained that he was innocent on the charge of cheating Fulke of twopence.

However, there was little to support Ailward's defence, and St Thomas did not put in an appearance on his behalf. Ailward refused to undergo the traditional form of trial – by combat – and the beadle refused to allow trial by fire, where the accused was required to hold a red-hot iron bar and was then tested as to how quickly the wounds healed. It was eventually decided that Ailward was to be tried by water, much as witches were in later years. He was found to be guilty.

Ailward was sentenced to undergo a most gruesome form of punishment that invariably ended in the death of the criminal. He was taken from Leighton Buzzard to a spot near Bedford, and then the executioner set to work. Ailward's eyes were cut out, while his hands and feet were sawn off. His dismembered body was then thrown to the ground where he was abandoned, left to die in great pain without friend or family to comfort him.

It so happened that a kind and godly burgess from Bedford named Eilbrecht was passing that way, and stopped to find out what had happened. His heart was filled with pity when he saw Ailward, for it seemed to him that the punishment was a horrible and savage one. Ailward may have been a bad man, but he did not deserve such terrible treatment.

Eilbrecht took him to his own house in Bedford, knelt down, and prayed for the life of the sinner. For days Ailward was in fever and it seemed that he was certain to die, but Eilbrecht continued to pray regularly for him. After a few more days it seemed that Ailward might still live, and he began to become conscious and alert.

Ailward realised, though, that he was in a terrible position. He was blind, while he had also lost both hands and feet. How could a man survive in such a condition? As he lay on Eilbrecht's bed, he felt full of sorrow and remorse and, taking his example from the good burgess of Bedford, also began to pray.

That night Ailward dreamt a powerful dream, so clear that it seemed to him to be a vision. He saw the Virgin Mary and St Thomas come into his room and look down upon his bed. St Thomas reached out, and with his staff touched Ailward's aching eye-sockets. Mary herself placed her holy hands upon his shattered arms and legs.

Imagine the shock and delight in Eilbrecht's household when it was discovered that new eyes had begun to grow in Ailward's head. Within a few weeks he could see again, while new hands and feet also developed.

The story caused quite a sensation, and Ailward recounted every detail to the parish priest. It was clear that a miracle had taken place and that Ailward's prayers to St Thomas had been granted. What had begun with the cheating of the poor Fulke had ended with Ailward a changed man. He did not return to Westoning. Instead he went to Canterbury, where his story was received with great joy, and he spent his last years as a pensioner in one of the many institutions there that catered to the cult of St Thomas.

Serpents and Sayings

LIKE most English counties, Bedfordshire had its own collection of sayings, recipes and folk medicines that had been passed down from one generation to another. Most of this store of folk 'wisdom' has now been forgotten, but odd fragments have survived.

In the 17th century, for example, there was even a Bedfordshire recipe for making serpents! Instructions were quite specific, but of course it may all have been a hoax by a contemporary who wished to deflate the wise old women of the county who placed great store on special potions. Whatever, if you wanted to make some serpents you needed to gather red sage in May, and to bring it in before any dew got onto it. The sage was bruised and crushed between the fingers before being put into a bottle.

The bottle, tightly sealed, then had to be placed inside a 'hot' dunghill of horse manure for 40 days, then recovered and placed in a 'lukewarm' oven. This would cause a large serpent to grow in the bottle, but of course such a creature could be highly dangerous. The 'cook' should therefore take the bottle out of the oven and plunge it into boiling water to ensure that the serpent was dead.

After this, the bottle could be broken open and the dead serpent baked in the oven until it had turned to powder. Finally, the cook should gather a group of friends and put the powder of the dead serpent on the fire – at which point all present would see serpents crawling up and down the walls of the room. One is tempted to conclude that anyone prepared to go through with this 'recipe' would probably be the type to see crawling serpents in their kitchen anyway!

A variety of more useful 'medical' methods were employed to cure the sick of Bedfordshire. Mr Gadbury of Dunstable spent nearly a year in bed in about 1735 due to severe headaches. Dr Freeman of Ampthill eventually came to his rescue with a potion of red sage and egg shells baked into a powder and mixed with ale; it is not recorded whether Mr Gadbury saw any serpents after this, but his headaches improved.

Dr Crawley of Dunstable was said to be an expert on earwigs. When a girl got one in her ear he advised her that it would bite and sting, and would breed if not dealt with within 24 hours. The doctor syringed the insect out of her ear.

The advice of the medical profession was beyond the financial reach of most ordinary folk, who had to rely upon traditional beliefs. Whatever the ailment, there was usually some folk cure to match it. In Dunstable, for example, measles was treated with a potion made by boiling marigolds in strong alcohol, then adding treacle.

Elsewhere in Bedfordshire, rheumatism was meant to be treated by rinsing your socks in whisky, though one presumes that the whisky did not have to be drunk afterwards. A concoction of hen manure and the pounded green skin of elder wood was said to be good for boils and abscesses.

There was also some Bedfordshire advice for the minor ailment of hiccups. The best thing was to repeat the following rhyme five times without breathing:

> 'Eee-cup, eee-cup, peek in another town;
> Five drops in a cup, good for the eee-cup.'

The country folk of the county had a store of sayings and superstitions to cover every eventuality. Many of these were also connected with times of the year and the rounds of the farming calendar. Seeds had to be sown and pigs killed before the moon was full, for to do either when the moon was on the wane was to ensure that something would go wrong. Anyone who saw a magpie had to bow or spit to ensure continued good fortune while the person who heard the first cuckoo of the year had to turn their money over or it would soon be lost. Many people kept bees in the old days, when honey was used as a sweetener instead of sugar; bees had to be kept happy by telling them all the family news and gossip, or they would fly away to find a more convivial host.

Other superstitions included those to do with the weather. A popular saying for amateur forecasters was 'Wet Friday, wet Sunday, wet week'. It was also believed that if the wind was in the east when it started to rain, then it would rain for the next three days. If a small patch of snow remained in a corner it was said to be 'yawning for more', so that another snow shower was bound to follow.

If a person dropped a knife it meant that a man would be coming to visit, and if a fork was dropped a woman would soon be at the door. However, to drop a spoon meant certain disappointment.

There were, of course, a number of beliefs concerning death. When someone died and was allowed to 'lie over' on Sunday before being buried the following week, then another death would occur in the village within the next seven days. One imagines that Bedfordshire undertakers were always kept busy on Saturdays! Once a person had been buried, the soil over the grave occasionally settled and subsided; this was considered to be a sure sign that Death was 'yawning for a relative'. When a farmer died it was customary to brick up his smock in the kitchen wall of the house – this was to provide him with clothes for his travels beyond the grave. Occasionally other items, such as shoes, were bricked up as well.

Some sayings were peculiar to Bedfordshire. These included the phrase 'as crooked as Weston Brook', which referred to the meandering stream of that name: incidentally, the water from this brook was said to be useful for curing skin diseases. Similar was the saying 'as crooked as Crawley' which was said to refer to Crawley Brook, once measured as taking 80 miles to travel what would have been 18 for the average crow. However, this phrase may also refer to the notorious 17th century official, Judge Crawley.

The most famous saying connected to Bedfordshire, at least in past centuries, was 'as plain as Dunstable Highway'. This was used to describe something that was obvious and clear. The phrase must have been well-known in the 16th century, for in a sermon before King Edward VI, Bishop Latimer referred to something as being 'plain Dunstable way' while John Heywood's *Proverbs* of 1546 mentions 'as playne as Dunstable hie way'. No doubt the saying is based on the clear and straight way that Watling Street takes through Dunstable.

A large number of sayings were created by adding various descriptions to the names of Bedfordshire villages. Thus we can get an idea of terms of abuse in eastern Bedfordshire from the names of 'Wicked Wilden', 'Wretched Ravensden', 'Ragged Renhold' and 'Cold Colmworth'. Needing more explanation is 'Keysoe Hogwash', since hogwash was the pot liquor that was normally given to the pigs – the implication being that Keysoe people were so poor or mean that they would drink anything!

Sometimes these comments on individual places were put into a rhyme:

'Sutton for mutton,
Potton for beef,
Gamlingay for pretty girls,
And Waresley for a thief.'

More palatable is the subject of Bedfordshire food. The county had its own version of the ploughman's lunch. The

Bedfordshire 'clanger' was a long suet dumpling filled with meat at one end and a sweet dessert at the other. The normal mixture was to have pork and onions for the 'first course' and jam for the 'afters'. This was very convenient for the ploughman, since he could eat his entire lunch with only one hand.

A particular rhyme was attached to the important job of doing the laundry, though it varied slightly from area to area throughout the county:

> 'They that wash on Monday
> Have all the week to dry,
> They that wash on Tuesday
> Are not so much awry.
> They that wash on Wednesday
> Are not so much to blame,
> They that wash on Thursday
> Wash for shame.
> They that wash on Friday
> Wash in need,
> And they that wash on Saturday
> Oh, they're sluts indeed!'

The Prisoners' Friend

THE town of Bedford has two well-known statues that commemorate the achievements of its most famous citizens, John Bunyan and John Howard. Both of these men had strong connections with prison life and both were motivated in their achievements by a powerful religious faith.

Although John Howard is always associated with Bedford, and Cardington in particular, he was in fact born in Hackney in about 1726. However his father, a successful upholsterer, owned property at Cardington and the young Howard spent much time there at the house of a tenant farmer. Eventually, though, this rural idyll was broken when John was sent to school in Hertford.

Howard's father arranged a London apprenticeship for him, but John gave this up when he inherited his father's wealth. He soon adopted the typically leisured lifestyle of a wealthy young man of the 18th century, taking life easy and spending his money on continental travel. However this pleasant interlude was cut short by the onset of illness; Howard moved out of London to rented rooms where he could be looked after by a kindly landlady – with whom he promptly fell in love, despite her being much older than himself. The young Howard understood the landlady's misgivings about their difference in

age, but in 1752 he managed to persuade her to marry him. The marriage was ended by her death in 1755.

Free of family commitments once more, Howard rekindled his love of travelling. In 1755 he decided to sail to Lisbon, but off the coast of northern France his ship was attacked and captured by a French privateer. Howard and his fellow travellers were tied up and taken by the French to the port of Brest, where they were thrown into a dungeon whilst the privateers assessed their ransom value. Howard and the others were soon moved to Carpaix, but since he was obviously a gentleman he received better treatment than many of the English crew – he could be ransomed for more. Eventually Howard was exchanged for a French officer who had been captured by the British, but he had seen many of his friends and colleagues die of prison fever and maltreatment. This experience was to haunt Howard for the rest of his life and was the powerful motive for his concern about the welfare of prisoners.

After these few bitter months, Howard seems to have lost interest in travel and instead decided to settle down on his estate at Cardington. He set about improving the farm and built new cottages for the labourers, before his attention wandered to other matters. In 1758 he married Henrietta Leeds, who came from Croxton in Cambridgeshire. Like Howard, she had a deep religious faith and sold many of her personal jewels to help the poor in the Cardington district. Henrietta died in 1765 after giving birth to a son who was to cause Howard many problems later in life.

During these more settled years at Cardington Howard was long enough in the district to build up important relationships and connections. He became very friendly with Samuel Whitbread and attended the Congregational chapel in Bedford, though he left it after an argument over infant baptism and helped to pay for a new chapel.

After a brief period of travel, Howard was appointed High Sheriff of Bedfordshire in 1773. This office brought him into close contact with the county's gaols, where he found many things to worry him. The gaols were usually run by a gaoler who received no salary, but made a living for himself by charging the prisoners fees and providing food and drink for a suitable profit. All prisoners who entered gaol thus got into debt with the gaoler – including those who were remanded in custody only to be found not guilty at trial. Unless debts and fees were paid, the gaoler would refuse to release anyone who had been entrusted into his care.

Prisons were also immoral and unhealthy places where vicious criminals, common debtors and dangerous lunatics could be mixed together. Toilet and washing facilities were almost non-existent though a rich man, prepared to pay the gaoler's fees, could enjoy a more comfortable lifestyle. In some prisons the death rate per annum was as high as one in every four prisoners whilst all convicts lived in fear of 'gaol fever' – typhus.

Howard was shocked by what he found in the Bedfordshire gaols and could perhaps understand the sufferings of the prisoners due to his own time in a French dungeon. He found, though, that the Bedfordshire justices were uninterested in the matter and he could not get them to see that it would be better to pay the gaoler a salary than to allow the fees system to continue. So Howard decided to make a study of English prisons by visiting as many as he could, recording and measuring whatever he found. One of the problems with these visits was that the smell of the prisons was so bad that it permeated his clothes and lingered for hours. Because of this he gave up travelling to and from prisons in the enclosed space of a carriage, preferring the fresh air of travel by horseback though for a time he tried using vinegar to counteract the smell. His notebook also picked up the prison stench, so he used to lay it out in front of the fire when he got home.

Howard visited many English prisons and his findings helped to influence Parliamentary debates on the subject. He was called to the bar of the House of Commons to receive thanks for his work. Two new laws were passed through the efforts of an MP named Popham, but they did not go far enough to satisfy all the improvements that Howard had requested. In particular, little was done about providing salaries for gaolers or for organising a proper system of inspection.

So Howard continued touring Britain to inspect all the gaols he could gain entry to, but at the back of his mind was always the threat of contracting 'gaol fever'. Indeed many neglectful magistrates, keen to excuse their ignorance of prison conditions, told him that prisons were simply too dangerous to be visited regularly.

During 1775 Howard broadened his perspective by visiting a number of prisons in Europe while in 1776 he made an inspection of the prison hulks moored on the Thames at Woolwich. All this contributed to his book, *The State of the Prisons,* which was published in 1777. In the book Howard pointed out the main problems with the prison system – the lack of water and sanitation, the scale of fees charged to prisoners, the lack of productive work for the inmates, the mixing of old and young or male and female, and the imprisonment of debtors.

He made his longest journey in 1781, when he went to Russia. There he witnessed the punishment of the 'knout', where criminals were tied to a post and whipped with a heavy, knotted rope – often causing their death.

By 1784 Howard was famous, having travelled 42,033 miles in his study of prisons. He was given the freedom of Liverpool and sightseers came to Cardington in the hope of meeting the great man or catching a glimpse of him. Sometimes Howard's servants were bribed to arrange an accidental meeting, but the best chance of seeing him was usually on a Sunday when he rode to chapel in Bedford.

Howard's obsessive concern with prisons had caused him to neglect his family duties and by this time there were obvious problems with his son. The son had been sent to Edinburgh University, but had become involved in various forms of vice; back at Cardington, he formed an unusual friendship with Howard's own assistant, Thomasson. Howard left his son at Cardington while he went on a visit to Greece, Venice and Vienna, but during his absence the son's behaviour worsened.

Samuel Whitbread, a family friend, had to send two men from an asylum to collect the youth and bring him home from one of his dubious excursions. When John Howard returned from his travels, the son tried to attack him.

In July 1787 John Howard left for his second trip to Russia. He travelled to Cherson to inspect military hospitals there, but was caught in a heavy rainstorm while riding on horseback and caught a chill, which proved to be fatal. He died on 20th January 1790 and was buried in a Russian burial ground near the village of Dauphigny.

Howard died long before his work was completed, for many of his recommendations were not put into practice until Sir Robert Peel's Prisons Act of 1823. Nonetheless, he succeeded in making the state of the prisons an issue for public debate at a time when the neglect of them was a national scandal. This was a substantial achievement in an age when human life was cheap and when the condition of the lower orders rarely concerned the wealthy or powerful at all. He is remembered to this day in the name of an organisation dedicated to furthering his aims – the Howard Reform League.

The Bedfordshire Tornado

BEDFORDSHIRE has been fortunate to have suffered very few serious natural disasters. As much of the area is low-lying, the most common problem has been with floods along the broad valley of the river Ouse. There was, for example, a bad flood in October 1607 when the river overflowed at Bedford and a woman was drowned.

Floods like this struck Bedfordshire quite regularly and were of little interest to the outside world. Nobody seemed especially concerned when in September 1797 villages like Chicksands and Shillingford were cut off from their local market town at Shefford for three days.

However, when much of Bedfordshire and some surrounding counties were devastated by a tornado in May 1950 the incident aroused widespread interest and was the subject of detailed study – for at the time the Meteorological Office was based in Dunstable and the weather men thus had a rather rude introduction to the subject of high winds!

The terrifying power of the tornado struck Bedfordshire during the afternoon of 21st May 1950. Strictly speaking, there were three tornadoes – one major one and two 'subsidiaries', all of which formed in the valleys of the Chiltern Hills after a spate of thunderstorms that day. The storms then advanced swiftly north-eastwards across Bedfordshire and into Cambridgeshire, battering the countryside with high winds, huge hailstones and torrential rain. By the time the storm had exhausted itself, over £50,000 worth of damage had been done over an area covering 65 miles of eastern England.

The weather forecast had stated that there would be 'fair periods and scattered thundery showers', but trouble began in the valleys that were etched into the north-west face of the Chiltern Hills around such places as Wendover in Buckinghamshire and Dunstable. The thunderstorms set up violent movements in the air, which then advanced across the countryside at a speed of about 25 knots, wreaking havoc as the tornado gathered strength and created a whirlwind effect.

The first places to be struck were in Buckinghamshire, at Wendover and Aston Clinton, but the storm began to reach its full devastating power as it arrived at the borders of Bedfordshire. The small town of Linslade was very badly hit, with 300 houses being damaged and a pigeon loft carried 300 yards. The whirlwind then lifted partially off the ground and this saved much of nearby Leighton Buzzard from devastation. The wind came back to ground level just as it left the town, causing damage along the road to Heath and Reach. Much of its energy was then used up in the countryside over the next few miles, with two cows being killed at Broom Hills Farm and a nursery being devastated at Shenley Hill, Reach.

The power of the tornado then lifted into the air again, and it passed over Woburn with very little damage at all. Lidlington also escaped lightly, with a few loose items being sucked out of houses by the whirlwind.

By the time the storm passed round the southern side of Bedford, it was having a devastating effect once more, with the wind reaching speeds of over 100 knots. At Harrowden Road it did much damage, while at Fenlake it destroyed a number of trees, uprooting them and carrying them bodily across the river Ouse. At Wyboston it damaged the Methodist chapel, but then passed over St Ives and into Cambridgeshire. The last place to be struck was Sutton, near Ely.

A subsidiary tornado began near Houghton Conquest, south of Bedford. This did a great deal of damage at Wilshampstead, battering Duck End Farm and also doing some damage at Goldington. At Putnoe Farm some horses were terrified by the storm.

The miracle of this tornado was that no-one was killed by it, perhaps because the torrential rain that fell before it struck drove everyone into shelter. A number of farm creatures were killed, though, including at least 500 chickens. However, various freak weather conditions accompanied the tornado and these claimed their victims.

The most serious loss of life was at Houghton Conquest, where two men and a bullock were killed by lightning. The two dead men were part of a party of five people from Kempston who had all been caught in the open when the thunderstorm struck; they were all rushing for cover when the lightning killed two of them, the other three needing hospital treatment. A shop in Leighton Buzzard was struck by lightning and set on fire.

The storm also brought torrential rain and freak hailstones to much of the county. The road from Bedford to Northampton was blocked by hailstones 18 inches in depth at Oakley, while those that fell at North Crawley were over six inches wide and weighed four ounces. The heaviest hailstones were reported as having fallen at Ascott Farm near Leighton Buzzard. Unconfirmed rumours claimed that there were drifts of hailstones at Turvey that blocked the road to a depth of three ft, and certainly there were six inch drifts at Dunstable. In some parts of Bedfordshire the hailstones were found to be a curious leaf-shape, though the weather experts explained this was due to several hailstones having been frozen together.

The heaviest rain fell between Milton Ernest and Turvey, but there was also very heavy rain at Shefford. At Chapel End Farm, Houghton Conquest, water in the duck pond apparently rose by ten ft. A little girl from Podington died in the north-east of the county near Pertenhall, when a normally placid stream was suddenly turned into a raging torrent and the vehicle in which she was travelling was swept away. There were floods of three feet deep in Kempston when the Ouse overflowed.

The fourth victim of the storm was 13 year old Anita Bullard, who was fatally injured near Bedford when her horse bolted in fright.

With such widespread devastation, the Government stepped in to help. The Ministry of Supply depot at Elstow was opened up so that 450 tarpaulins could be distributed to help where houses had been damaged. A national collection was also organised to assist people from the worst hit areas.

Fire at Luton Hoo

A FEW miles to the south of Luton, standing amidst pleasant Chiltern hills, is the mansion of Luton Hoo. It is a house with a chequered history, having once been owned by a strongly-detested Prime Minister and, in 1843, the scene of a disastrous fire.

Luton Hoo was a fairly unspectacular country house when it was bought by the third Earl of Bute in 1762, but he did acquire 4,500 acres of land with it. Bute had become Prime Minister to the erratic George III the previous year, and unkind critics said he had bought this country estate to keep a safe distance between himself and the London mob.

Bute set about improving the house and commissioned the famous architect Robert Adam to rebuild it. Improvements were continued by his heirs and successors, who built up great family wealth based on their interests in the South Wales coal industry during the time of the second Marquis of Bute. By 1842 Adam's improvements had been further added to by Smirke, and the whole mansion – with its contents – was insured for the huge sum of £58,950. The enormity of this sum can be compared to the wages of the labourers on the Luton Hoo estate, who would have been pleased to earn more than £40 in a year.

However even such a magnificent mansion and such a powerful family were not safe from disaster. On 8th November 1843 some plumbers came to work on the roof above the hall.

While they were working on the copper roof it seems that sparks fell through crevices in the metal, onto the wooden rafters beneath. Though staff from the house came up to check their work and to ensure all was safe, the sparks slumbered undetected beneath the copper roof, waiting only the opportunity to burst into all-consuming fire.

Though the Marquis was away on business at Cardiff, where the docks bore the family name, the house was still staffed with many of his employees. At about 2 am on 10th November 1843 one of these, an under-gardener who slept in one of the basement rooms, heard a sound like the cracking of a whip. Disturbed from his sleep and curious what the sound was, he looked out of the window and saw the light of a fire flickering in the darkness. Raising the alarm that the roof over the great hall was on fire, he roused all the staff in the house and frantic activity broke out at Luton Hoo.

Someone was sent to summon the fire engines from Luton and Hitchin, while Mr Thompson, the farm manager, organised a workforce of farm labourers. Though first to arrive, the Luton fire engine proved to be too small to have a worthwhile effect while that from Hitchin arrived with too little water.

Luton Hoo was unusual for a house at the time in having a supply of water piped to it, but in the confusion someone broke the pumps. There was thus no water to supply the fire engines, without sending them a quarter of a mile to one of the ornamental ponds. Eventually the pipe that led from the pond to the house was dug up, and this provided some water – but not enough to save much of the house.

Meanwhile, in the house itself, the fire was spreading rapidly. The copper roof over the entrance hall melted, the chapel was engulfed and the library threatened. One wing of the house could not be saved from the voracious flames, but in the hope of saving the south wing a partition wall was pulled down.

One of the greatest features of the house was the library. This was 146 ft long and divided into three rooms. It contained a large number of valuable paintings and over 40,000 books. Mrs Partridge, the housekeeper, knew that the paintings were the most valuable possessions in the house and directed her staff to the ones which were the greatest priority for rescuing. She helped cut down the canvasses using a case knife while pointing out the best pictures in turn to her helpers. Nearly everything of value was saved from the library by being carried outside.

The Bute family solicitor, Mr Chase, organised some men to help him rescue sculptured marble mantlepieces from several rooms. As the last of these expensive items was being taken from the room, its ceiling collapsed – had this occurred a few seconds earlier, the men would have been trapped in the fire.

When dawn came it was apparent that much of the house had been lost. The great hall, with its noble Ionic columns, was gone, as was the chapel – where a beautiful Venetian altar piece had been destroyed.

The loss of Luton Hoo hit the headlines and *The Times* sent a man to describe the scene. He found 'a mass of smoking ruins' set amidst a beautiful landscape. The mansion itself presented a 'melancholy spectacle, blackened, dismantled and fast falling into ruins'.

Local people had rallied round to help during the night and the reporter commented, rather patronisingly, that 'the peasantry and townspeople deserve great praise for their conduct'. Food and drink had been set out for the exhausted workers, but this opportunity was abused by some of the idle and curious who were attracted to the scene. Some of them got drunk and hampered attempts to salvage the contents of the house.

Other curious bystanders decided to investigate the ruins and actually got inside the still-smouldering house. One man went to examine the burnt-out remains of the billiard room, which had been said – before the fire – to be fire-proof. As he walked across its floor the boards collapsed and he was suddenly 'immersed in a bed of burning particles' though he was not seriously hurt.

The fire marked the end of an era for Luton Hoo. The Marquis sold the remains to Mr Ward, who resold it to Mr Leigh of Liverpool. Under Leigh's control much of the house was rebuilt. In 1903 it was sold again, this time to Sir Julius Wernher – who rebuilt it again, so that Luton Hoo eventually came to have little similarity to the house that had stood before the disastrous fire of 1843.

Murder at Deadman's Hill

THE most famous murder in Bedfordshire history is probably that of Michael Gregsten, a scientist in his mid thirties, near the village of Clophill in 1961. Yet the name of Gregsten has been largely forgotten by all except afficionados of crime stories, for the case will always be remembered by the name of the road beside which Gregsten was killed – the A6. The man who was convicted of the crime, James Hanratty, was executed at Bedford Prison in April 1962 but his name has continued to be surrounded by controversy – continual doubts over the justice of his conviction helped to undermine support for capital punishment, making his case one of national importance.

Few of those involved in the case had any connection with Bedfordshire, and it was a complex and fateful path that brought them to the aptly-named Deadman's Hill. Michael Gregsten, aged 36, was a scientist with something of the reputation of a playboy. In 1961 he was separated from his wife and family but had formed a relationship with a colleague at work, Valerie Storie, who was 13 years his junior.

On the evening of 22nd August 1961 the couple drove to a pub at Dorney, near Windsor, in Gregsten's Morris 1000 car. After a drink they parked the car in a field near the river Thames that was a popular haunt of courting couples. They were surprised by a sudden tapping on the car window, and shocked to see a gun pointed at them. At gunpoint, Gregsten accepted instructions that he should drive as the man directed and started the car moving; Miss Storie was told to sit in the back, from where she could see little of the stranger with the gun.

Gregsten was given directions as to where to drive which suggested that the stranger had no real purpose to his movements. At first they went to Slough, where they stopped for petrol and later on halted at a milk machine but on neither occasion did the stranger get out of the car.

The car took the A5 away from London to St Albans and as it progressed northwards Gregsten tried to attract attention by flashing the reversing light, but no other travellers reacted to this confusing message. At St Albans they took the A6 and continued into Bedfordshire through the middle of the night.

After passing through the village of Clophill, Gregsten was directed to pull into a lay-by at the side of the A6. Although no-one in the car knew it, this spot was known as Deadman's Hill. The car pulled up at the brow of the hill, and Gregsten was directed to turn it round so that it was facing back towards London. The purpose of this apparently aimless journey into the middle of nowhere, only to turn round again, is one of the unsolved mysteries of the case.

The stranger then shot Gregsten twice in the head, apparently without any justification. He raped Miss Storie, before forcing her to drag Gregsten's body out of the car and dump it in the field beside the road. He turned away and back towards the car, apparently intending to leave her with the dead man, but then came back and shot Valerie Storie five times. Badly injured and with her spine shattered, she pretended to be dead.

The stranger had earlier asked for instructions about how to drive the Morris 1000, and now he headed off towards London. Valerie Storie was found at about 6.30 am; a young man preparing for a traffic census made some brief notes of her description of the killer.

Later that morning a Morris 1000 was seen in Redbridge, north-east London, where its erratic passage attracted the attention of a lorry driver; it was later found abandoned in

Ilford. On 24th August a woman living at Old Knebworth was threatened with a gun by a man who many assumed to be the A6 murderer, but the murder weapon was actually found that evening hidden behind the seat of a London bus.

The first man to be picked up on suspicion of being the murderer was Peter Alphon, who had attracted attention through his strange behaviour at an hotel in Finsbury Park. Alphon wove a complicated story about his movements. He fitted the description given initially by Miss Storie, but she failed to pick him out from an identity parade on 24th September when she was still recovering from medical treatment. There was suspicion, however, that Alphon was involved in an attack in Richmond on 7th September.

Attention switched to James Hanratty, a London petty criminal who had made several phone calls to Detective Superintendent Acott, the officer in charge of the case. Cartridges from the murder weapon were found in a room at the Vienna Hotel in Maida Vale where Hanratty had stayed the night before the murder – but it is one of the curious twists of the case that Alphon had also stayed in the same room the night after the murder. Hanratty had boasted to other underworld characters that the back of a bus seat was a good hiding place. Another unusual element is that the widowed Mrs Gregsten had already seen Hanratty and claimed to have felt intuitively that he was the killer.

Hanratty caused problems for himself by attempting to cover up his life of petty crime at the risk of confusing his own defence against a far more serious charge. Valerie Storie identified him at an identity parade because he pronounced the word 'thinking' as 'finking'. The striking colour of his eyes was another factor in her identification. However, he did not resemble the identikit picture built up from her descriptions.

Hanratty failed to produce an effective alibi, at first claiming that he had been in the company of criminals at the time of the murder and so could not produce witnesses. He then changed his story to explain that he had been in Liverpool, and a sweetshop owner supported this. He later added a further explanation that he had been staying that night in Rhyl in North Wales, and described the room where he slept though he could not recall the address. This version of his story was not immediately examined. But perhaps the greatest mystery is about Hanratty's ability to drive a car; he had been a regular car thief for some time, so it would be surprising if he had had to ask Miss Storie for advice about how to change the gears in the Morris 1000.

Hanratty was tried at Bedford in a hearing that lasted 21 days, making it the longest criminal hearing in English legal history at the time. Miss Storie was adamant that Hanratty was the killer and the jury was certainly given the impression that Hanratty had something to hide by the confusion over his alibi; he claimed that he had not said anything about staying in Rhyl as he could not remember where he had slept and thought this might go against him. In his summing up, the judge was cautiously supportive of Hanratty but after ten hours the jury decided that Hanratty was guilty.

There was an immediate appeal against the verdict and the sentence of death, but this was dismissed on 14th March 1962. Admidst talk of a petition for his reprieve, Hanratty was executed at Bedford on 4th April 1962.

The case, though, did not die with Hanratty. A criminal on the fringes of the story, Charles France, committed suicide on 16th March just after the appeal was dismissed; it was this man who had told police about Hanratty's supposed hiding place on the buses. Alphon, safely in France, wrote a confession that he and France had framed Hanratty as part of a complex plot. He argued that the whole story had begun with Mrs Gregsten hiring some thugs to frighten her husband out of the relationship with Miss Storie.

At the end of the 1990s the A6 murder and the fate of Hanratty continued to be in the news and the subject of legal argument. There is a growing feeling that his conviction was unsafe, and further doubts have been expressed about the identification process involving Miss Storey and the disregarding of evidence from Rhyl. Perhaps a final solution to this mystery will soon be available.